LIVING
WITH LOSS

BOOKS BY RENE NOORBERGEN

Living With Loss
The Deathcry of an Eagle
Nostradamus—Invitation to a Holocaust
Secrets of the Lost Races
The Soul Hustlers
Programmed to Live
The Ark File
Charisma of the Spirit
Ellen G. White, Prophet of Destiny
You Are Psychic
Jeane Dixon—My Life & Prophecies

LIVING WITH LOSS

A Dramatic New Breakthrough
in Grief Therapy

Dr. RONALD W. RAMSAY

RENE NOORBERGEN

WILLIAM MORROW AND COMPANY, INC.
New York   *1981*

Library of Congress Cataloging in Publication Data

Ramsay, Ronald W
    Living with loss.

    Includes bibliographical references and index.
    1. Loss (Psychology) 2. Psychotherapy. I. Noorbergen, Rene, joint author. II. Title. [DNLM:
1. Grief. 2. Behavior therapy. 3. Attitude to death.
BF 575.G7 / R181L]
RC572.L65R35   616.89'142   81-756
ISBN 0-688-00485-7   AACR1

Printed in the United States of America

3   4   5   6   7   8   9   10

BOOK DESIGN BY BERNARD SCHLEIFER

To Rita

Foreword

STRESS FLOWS FROM EVERY kind of human activity. It is responsible for many of today's diseases and can be a critical factor in death.

Several years ago I developed a normally fatal cancer, a tumor that originated under the skin of my thigh. I immediately underwent surgery and cobalt therapy. However, I was told I would not live beyond one year. Nevertheless, I was determined to continue living and working without worrying unduly about the outcome.

I rewrote my will, including in it several suggestions for the continuation of my work by my colleagues. Having taken care of that business, I forced myself to disregard thoughts about dying. I immersed myself in my work—and I survived.

Somehow my conscious decision to cut down the initial stress that set in when I was informed of my condition helped my system fight the normally fatal cancer. Stress plays a much more important role in our lives than is often realized and we can greatly benefit from a deeper understanding of the role of stress in life. Yet an investigation into stress is meaningful only if it is realized that, by definition, stress is the nonspecific response of the body to any demand, and hence it is present whenever an organism is called upon to readjust or adapt in order to maintain normalcy. It is irrelevant whether an agent or situation provoking stress is pleasant or unpleasant—all can induce the physiological manifestations of stress in the body.

Sudden death has occurred as a consequence of violent arguments with supervisors or the emotional upset of witnessing serious accidents; however, in addition to painful occurrences, sudden reunion with long-lost relatives, triumphs or the happy ending of some event that is particularly meaningful to us may also lead to sudden death.

In this excellent book on grief therapy, Dr. Ramsay and Mr. Noorbergen have thoroughly reviewed grief therapy and its relation to stress. The book is written in a direct and practical style; the authors have given us not only a unified analysis of this important topic, but also a clear outline of the detrimental effects of severe stress on the human body. I endorse this book without hesitation.

HANS SELYE, C.C., M.D., Ph.D., D.Sc.
President
International Institute of Stress
Montreal, Canada

Acknowledgments

Intense bereavement has been an inseparable part of the human experience since the beginning of time. To be instrumental in introducing a new therapy that promises hope for those to whom life itself seems to have ended is a joyous experience.

Many have added their expertise to the creation of this book, and to them I owe a debt of gratitude. To name the research reports that provided much of the scientific background for the book would fill pages. Inasmuch as most of them have already been credited in various ways within the text and notes of the book, I should like to limit my remarks to those individuals who have been especially helpful in the development of the manuscript, as well as in its final production.

I wish to express my appreciation to Dr. Paul DeVivo and Dr. Rod Fowler of the University of Tennessee for sharing their insights and psychological counseling techniques. Their lectures made it possible for me to gain an even greater knowledge of the history of grief therapy. My wife, Judie, added much to the development of the manuscript in many different ways. As an active collaborator and constructive critic, she is second to none.

I also wish to take this opportunity to express my most sincere appreciation to my editor, Elizabeth Frost Knappman, for the painstaking attention both she and her editorial assistant, Kate Kelly, have given to the final manuscript. Working with them has been both a pleasure and a most productive experience.

Collegedale, Tennessee
February 5, 1981

Contents

Introduction

As I WATCHED the CBS-TV program "60 Minutes" one Sunday evening, I found myself engrossed in a program on grief therapy, employing a dramatic new method developed by Dr. Ronald W. Ramsay of the University of Amsterdam's Phobia Clinic.

I became fascinated, for while other books and theories on bereavement deal mainly with grief surrounding the moment of death, the demonstrated Guided Confrontation Therapy (GCT) was aimed at solving pathological bereavement problems of long standing.

The program set a chain reaction of events in motion that ended in a meeting with Dr. Ramsay in Amsterdam and a quiet week of probing into the potential of this new method, resulting in an agreement that led to the writing of this book.

Guided Confrontation Therapy is a relatively new development in behavior therapy, but its impact is already spreading throughout the Western world via Dr. Ramsay's lectures and workshops.

The therapy is *different*—some people even call it harsh— but it contains a message of hope because, as a result of this new concept, thousands of people who are caught in the unrelenting vise of mental anguish and unconsolable grief can now be offered a helping hand.

In Guided Confrontation Therapy the patient is directed to recall all the distressing emotions that form part of the intense bereavement and relive them to the fullest. Every negative emotion that is connected with the loss is carefully brought to the surface, and the emotional outbursts that invariably follow are prolonged as long as needed—drowning the patient in tears —until the emotions are totally extinguished and there are no more tears left. The heart-tearing cry of a mother looking for the first time at a picture of her deceased little girl; the wife holding on to the experiences shared with her former husband; the agonizing memories of one's first stillborn baby or the loss of fortune or homeland; even the trauma caused by the disfigure-ment of a mastectomy can all be extinguished through Guided Confrontation Therapy. Resolving all of the negative emotions that together form the experience we know as "bereavement" will eventually lead to an acceptance of the reality of the loss, making it possible for the patient—now *ex*-griever—to reintegrate herself into life.

Unlike other forms of therapy, Guided Confrontation Ther-apy does not depend on insight as a prerequisite to change. In fact, in this way it differs drastically from other approaches and treatments, specifically with psychoanalysis, (where it is held that insight has to precede a change in behavior.)

The studies conducted at the Amsterdam Phobia Clinic have shown that persons suffering from pathological grief are very similar to phobics in the development and maintenance of their problem. In treating phobics, the intake interview will usually reveal the nature of their problem; phobics usually *know* the situations that will bring on their fear. With pathological grief, however, it is not always that simple. Every case of grief con-sists of a number of phases and components such as shock, despair, guilt, anxiety, shame, etc., and in Guided Confronta-tion Therapy the stimulus situations that cause these negative feelings are brought to the surface, and the constant and re-peated confrontation that follows will eventually make them fade away. The therapy will not attempt to deny that the loss has indeed occurred, but it will make it more acceptable without the pain)

From the very first session on, there is a firm agreement between the therapist and the client as to exactly *what* needs to be done, *how* it is to be done, and *how and why it will progress.* And no attempts are made during the course of the therapy to help the patient gain insight as to the exact causes of his or her disturbance. *The primary concern of GCT is to extinguish the negative feelings and make it possible for the sufferer to begin a new life.* To show the client the irrationality of his action is useless. Many people caught in an unresolved grief situation are suffering from hallucinations, irrational beliefs, unwanted and unexplained fears, anxieties, etc., and they do not ask for insight; they ask for help and they want it NOW! GCT does not aim at breaking down irrational ideas. The therapy simply elicits the extremely painful feelings connected with the loss, and the confrontation that follows eventually leads to extinction.

There is, however, one serious warning.

This type of treatment is not suitable for everyone with bereavement problems. Grief is a normal reaction to loss. Only if the "working through" of the bereavement becomes stunted in some way should this treatment be considered.

The treatment is, however, ideally suited for a self-help approach, for individuals who find themselves in need of help but do not as yet feel the necessity to ask for professional counsel.

RENE NOORBERGEN
Collegedale, Tenn.
November 1980

LIVING
WITH LOSS

CHAPTER ONE

Grief: Life's Unavoidable Companion

WITH A SOLEMN LOOK on his tired face, the fifty-nine-year-old college president ascended the rostrum to deliver his farewell address.

It was a sad occasion indeed.

Differences with the faculty, charges of faltering leadership and a torrent of unsupported innuendoes had finally forced him to relinquish the one position he treasured most. With a quivering and unsteady voice, he fought his way through the presentation of his valedictory, and with an almost imperceptible sigh of relief he reached the last few lines . . .

> "I am driven forward into an unknown land
> The pass grows steeper
> The air colder and sharper
> A wind from my unknown destination stirs
>   the strings of expectation
> Still the question: Shall I ever get there?"

For a brief moment it seemed as if his mind were hovering on the brink of still another thought—and perhaps it was—but then his eyes slowly lost their sparkle. Hesitantly, stepping back from the podium, he sank to his knees, whimpering his last breath before the horrified eyes of the stricken audience and the stunned Board of Governors who had forced his ouster. His closest friend, a physician, hurriedly scaled the podium and with trembling hands reached out to administer aid, but recognizing the all-too-familiar face of death, he too collapsed and died.[1]

Was it grief that caused their deaths? Some say it was. We will never know. (But research is beginning to accept the uncomfortable connection between mind and body and the degree to which intense grief plays havoc with the flesh.

Doris Kearns wrote in *Lyndon Johnson and the American Dream* that the President's last years in office were filled with mounting frustration, disappointment and disgust.[2] Unable to resolve these feelings as President, he retired under a deluge of criticism for his Vietnam policy. Retreating to his native Texas, deprived of both power and political influence—the elements of politics he coveted most of all—Johnson looked back with pride at the few constructive domestic programs he had created during his time in the White House.

One evening, while discussing Richard Nixon's threats to cut off funds for some of Johnson's initiated programs, the former President sadly compared the plight of the Great Society programs to a starving woman.

"And when she dies," he mused with a look of intense distress on his face, "I will die too."

Not long thereafter, on January 20, 1973, Richard M. Nixon was inaugurated for a second term, and on the following day, January 21, his Administration announced the complete and total dismantling of the Great Society programs.

The very next day, January 22, Lyndon Johnson died of a heart attack. . . .

His words had been prophetic indeed, even though they had not been intended that way.

It was as if he had had a premonition of the intense grief the killing of his favorite programs would cause and, unknowingly, had used it to pinpoint the moment of his death.

Did his "death wish" hasten his demise? We will never know. But that there is a connection between grief and death is as undeniable as life itself.

Let's take a look at another example.

The death of Louis "Satchmo" Armstrong on July 6, 1971, sent tremors of distress throughout the music world. Everyone loved him and everyone would miss him. For a few days the world was saddened. But soon Arab terrorist attacks in Tel Aviv and the new SALT talks in Helsinki replaced Armstrong in the news, and he was forgotten. But not by his widow. There is no way of knowing how deeply she was shaken by the death of her beloved "Satchmo." The intensity of her overwhelming grief escaped just about everyone who came into contact with her—until she agreed to play the piano at a memorial concert honoring her late husband.

Her trembling hands were still hovering over the keyboard of the grand piano, playing the final chords of "St. Louis Blues," when she was stricken with a heart attack.

The notion of connections among bereavement, grief and death is as old as recorded history. Bereavement is a term used to describe the state a person finds himself in after losing a significant person—usually a spouse, parent, child or other family member. Grief, on the other hand, is the bodily, emotional and psychological reaction that the bereaved manifests in response to the loss.

Ancient documents tell of people suddenly dying in the grip of uncontrollable rages, intense grief or deep humiliation. In fact, ancient superstition subscribed to the idea that sudden deaths were at times divinely ordered.

One of the classic examples of biblical times is the case of the sudden deaths of Ananias and Sapphira who, on the verge of becoming Christians, lied to Peter about having turned over all the money they had received for the sale of their holdings.

Barely had Peter told him, "Thou hast not lied unto men but unto God," when Ananias dropped dead at his feet.

Three hours later, Ananias' widow repeated the lie. When in reply Peter commented, "Behold, the feet of them which have buried thy husband are at the door and they shall carry thee out," she too fell down and "yielded up the ghost." [3]

Throughout the development of medical science, the concept that sudden deaths were often associated with intense grief was widely accepted. But with the discovery of the germ and the virus in the late nineteenth century, the idea fell into disrepute and disappeared from scientific literature.

When Harvard physiologist Walter Cannon reintroduced the concept in 1942, suggesting a possible connection between voodoo and sudden death, the interrelationship between mental health and physical well-being began to arouse the curiosity of the scientific world all over again. An important step in this direction was made in the late 1960s, when a number of physicians, among them Dr. Arthur Smale, Dr. William Greene, and Dr. George Engel of the University of Rochester, New York, began to develop a file describing patients who had died suddenly after coming to what was described as an impasse in their lives. Their studies strongly suggested that the link between sudden death and stress was even stronger than previously suspected.

All the findings up to this point, however, were no more than "learned" suggestions until Curt Richter, physiologist at Johns Hopkins University, took up the challenge and embarked on a unique experiment. He took a number of healthy wild rats, clipped off their whiskers so as to increase their feeling of helplessness, and tied them into a bag so that they could not move. Next he dumped them into a tank filled with water and waited. . . . At first the rats attempted to keep their heads above water or stay afloat, as most rats would, but without whiskers to guide them and not being able to move freely within the bag, they soon stopped swimming and sank to the bottom. *Subsequent autopsies revealed that they had all died of cardiac arrest rather than drowning!* Their hearts were engorged with blood and their lungs were dry, indicating that drowning had not been the cause of their deaths, but possibly fear and hopelessness.

At a 1973 conference sponsored by the Harry Frank Guggenheim Foundation in New York City, anthropologist Jane Goodall projected a series of slides she had recently received from her associates located at the field station at the Gombi Stream Game Reserve in Tanzania.

"The sequence concerned the death of one of the important senior females in the community, Flo, a chimpanzee. Chimpanzees do not treat the death of one of their members casually; they appear to have a rather characteristic, apparently almost ritual and considered response to the event. This death particularly hurt Flo's son, Flint, who had always been unusually attached to her.

"The final slide showed Flint leaving the group. His shoulders, his posture, the general slackness of his body, even from the rear, even from a distance, clearly betrayed his misery.

"It was the last photo taken of him, because several days later he was found near where his mother had died. An autopsy was performed on him too; his death had been caused by a common virus infection, normally benign. Apparently, Flint, a young healthy animal, had died of grief!" [4]

When a human infant is separated from his mother, the pattern of response he displays consists of protest—after all, he is yearning for his mother—despair and eventually detachment. If this separation continues for a long time, it may result in serious psychological and even physiological problems. This condition is known as "anaclitic depression"—the breaking of a bond of dependency—and may be the prototype of human grief.

Was this perhaps Flint's condition after the death of his mother?

Many studies support this idea. Laboratory studies conducted on young monkeys have produced fascinating results. In some of these tests, the young monkey was separated from his mother and placed in solitary confinement and was only allowed to associate with other monkeys of the group on a very limited basis. In other experiments, the mother was taken away from the group, leaving the infant monkey alone with his playmates.

The most conclusive results came from an experiment where the mother of a pigtail monkey was taken away from her infant son. After some protest, the little monkey began to withdraw from all contact with the others, finally sitting all alone, hunched in a ball. When his face could be seen, "It had the same appearance of dejection and sadness that Darwin (1872) described and believed to be 'universally and instantly recognized as that of grief.' " Like Flint and Flo, the pigtail monkeys form very strong mother-child relationships, and with his mother gone, the little pigtail felt lost, utterly lost.[5]

When this strong attachment bonding exists, the results are as dramatic as when the roles are reversed and the young infants are taken away from their mothers.

One scientific investigator encountered two rhesus monkeys in the jungle who were carrying their dead babies with them until nothing remained but their skins and skeletons. Still another report described a female gorilla who carried her dead baby for four days before she finally dropped it on the trail, moving on alone, without child.[6]

Grief reactions are undoubtedly present in all species of the higher primates.

In a recent interview, Dr. Hans Selye, founder of the International Institute of Stress and world-renowned expert in this field, shared some of his findings with us.

"The stress everyone talks so much about is something very few people have adequately researched," he said in his soft, Viennese-accented voice. "It is impossible to pick up a newspaper or listen to a television program and come away without hearing something about stress, but even though there is considerably more worry about stress today than there was in the past, I really doubt whether modern men and women experience more stress than did their ancestors.

"But let's define stress before we continue.

"In simple medical terms, it is the nonspecific response of the body to any demand made on it. Stress is the state you are in, not the agent that produces it. That is what we call the stressor. Take temperature differences as an example. Cold and heat are stressors, and the body experiences the stress because of them. What we all must remember is that all the demands we make on our body—no matter which part of the body it is—cause stress. Even under deep anesthesia, when our emotions are not involved, the body still experiences stress. The stress that exists prior to the surgery will remain and even increase because of the changing body conditions, the blood loss, fluid changes and the glandular disturbances. The body fights for survival throughout the surgical procedure.

"Years ago there was no threat of nuclear war, but there was the ever-present danger of the plague, which destroyed whole populations. We still have many of the same stressors they had, but our age has added something to them; it's called social stress. I usually call it a loss of motivation, a sort of spiritual malady that by now has assumed almost epidemic proportions among the youth."

Dr. Selye paused for a moment and, pointing to his books on the shelves lining his office, continued:

"The most important discovery in this area was made in 1940, when it was revealed that if the organs involved in creating resistance to stress are malfunctioning, there will be a likelihood that disease will develop."

"Then," we asked, "you hold the position that stress can lead to disease and that this stress-induced disease can bring on sudden death?"

Dr. Selye nodded.

"There's not the slightest doubt about that. You can be bothered by people or events to the point that you begin to suffer hypertension and gastric ulcers and all the rest. Haven't you heard people say, 'It gives me a pain in the neck!' or 'It gives me a migraine headache!'? It can actually happen that way. Of course, these are among the more obvious results, but once you are chronically exposed to these stressors, it may result in the development of a serious disease. Among these are the typical stress diseases such as heart attacks, mental breakdowns, hypertension, cardiovascular diseases, etc.

"Believe me, stress can and does shorten your life!" [7]

In talking to Dr. Selye it is hard to imagine that he is the man who has bridged the gap between total ignorance about stress and the recognition of the role of stress through his pioneering research. Yet even though the detrimental effects of stress were already suspected as early as the 1940s, no one tied in stress with grief until the 1960s. Was it because death and grief were taboo subjects that were most carefully kept out of all polite and considered discussions—especially in front of children? Or was it because people had a general aversion to all things connected with sadness and grief?

Whatever the reason, it did not fit into the puritanical attitudes that still governed the first part of the twentieth century, but with the invasion of the social revolution of the sixties, the taboo was gradually lifted, so that by now death, grief, loss and other related issues have become the subject of numerous books. It is as if the mental healing profession has suddenly discovered a totally new field of interest without which our Western culture simply cannot exist.

Grief, however, is not limited to the emotional experience that comes in the aftermath of death. Sigmund Freud once characterized the grief reaction as a "profound painful dejection, loss of the capacity to love, inhibition of all activity, and a loss of interest in the outside world insofar as it does not recall the dead one." But it does not require a deep study of Freud or of the work of any other psychologist or psychoanalyst to realize that grief is an experience that becomes a dormant part of life at the very moment of birth. The loss of a significant object, be it a close relative, a marriage relationship, a lover, a part of the body, a valued possession, wealth or position can be an extremely grief-creating experience that can occur in everyone's lifetime and on a number of occasions. Every change we experience—whether it be leaving school, changing occupations, graduation, moving to another city or another country—is accompanied by a feeling of bereavement, for we always leave something behind to which we are attached.

Many of today's stresses are the result of careful deliberations, but when the stress is caused by a sudden loss, the human psyche suddenly finds itself confronted with a stress reaction we know as bereavement, and when that sets in, the body's defense system rapidly moves into action!

In a series of physiological countermeasures not as yet fully understood, the entire system is mobilized into what medical science recognizes as the *alarm stage*. Realizing the inherent danger of the stressor on the human body, chemical changes begin to take place in rapid succession. Sodium chloride levels in the extracellular fluids of the body begin to fall, while the potassium content rises. Blood glucose declines too, but restores itself to its normal level after a short period. It is at this precise point that the body begins to *react and resist*, forcing the blood levels to return to normal, and with the release of more ACTH the human system launches its counterattack against the factors causing the stress situation.

Up to this point, there is no acute danger, as these stages occur frequently in life and are not considered overly harmful. But when the stressor is not taken away, or, as in the case of intense and overwhelming grief, steps are not being taken to work through the bereavement process, then trouble may follow. It is here that Dr. Selye feels our own attitude toward the stressor plays an important role.

"Rather than relying on drugs or other techniques," he counsels, "I think there's another, better way to handle stress, which involves taking a different attitude toward the various events in our lives. Attitude determines whether we perceive any experience as pleasant or unpleasant," he points out, "and adopting the right one can convert a negative stress into a positive one—something I call a 'eustress,' employing the same Greek prefix for 'good' that occurs in such words as 'euphoria' and 'euphonia.' " [8]

But let's assume that the stressor is *not* taken away, and Dr. Selye's advice is ignored. Then what?

Science tells us the answer.

Unable to defeat the stressor, the body begins to "scream" for help, for relief—but often the damaging stressor increases its relentless pressure. The so-called *stage of body resistance* begins to dissipate and the *stage of exhaustion* sets in. Unable to keep up the uneven fight, the adrenal gland soon becomes totally depleted of cholesterol. There follows a hemorrhage into the cortex, and the formation of the life-supporting ACTH comes to a threatening halt. Simultaneously, the levels of sodium, chloride and glucose continue to sink lower and lower while the potassium and phosphate levels continue to rise . . . and suddenly it's all over. Tired and totally exhausted and poisoned by the chemical imbalance of the blood, the body system surrenders to the inevitable, and succumbs to death from exhaustion.

Stress has claimed another victim.

Of course, a situation such as described above would be an ultimate reaction to a case of ultimate stress, and most people do not go through this, even in cases of grief. The stress that is involved in an emotional crisis leading to a life-threatening situation will naturally depend heavily on the severity of the precipitating circumstances and is seldom carried to this point.

Yet it also goes the other way.

Dr. Selye's distinction between stress and distress—the latter being the type that hurts—can also be applied to situations that may appear entirely advantageous to the individual. The winner in a lottery whose lifestyle changes completely and deteriorates into an existence without his previous goals, the employee who is promoted to a function that is beyond his capacity, the moving of a lower-middle-class family into a high-class neighborhood, or the acceptance of a leading position by a member of a minority race in a previously all-white company may lead to unhealthy distress instead of the beneficial stress as outlined by Dr. Selye. The end results can often be disastrous.

Those who experience a transformation in lifestyle because of a much-desired change in their social or economic status are usually unaware of the stresses that accompany these changes. They will therefore be unable to view the departure from their former activity or status as a "loss" and the cause of a potential grief reaction. That this will express itself in one way or another is, however, a strong possibility.

During recent years, there has been a heightened interest in the human fear of being left alone. This basic anxiety is inseparable from bereavement. In order to understand this process, a familiarity with childhood grief is necessary.

A number of years ago it was believed that childhood grief was a short-lived thing, and that once the mother and the child had been separated from each other for a reasonable length of time, the child would soon forget his mother and get over his feelings of loss. Instead, like the little pigtail monkey referred to earlier, children, after an initial period of protest, become quieter, and withdrawn and less sociable.

The psychologist J. A. Robertson, who for twenty-five years made a special study of the practical implication of separation, writes:

"If a child is taken from his mother's care at this age [between eighteen and twenty-four months], when he is possessively and passionately attached to her, it is as if his world had been shattered. His intense need of her is unsatisfied, and the frustration and longing may send him frantic with grief. It takes an exercise of imagination to sense the intensity of his distress. He is as overwhelmed as any adult who has lost a beloved person by death. To the child of two with his lack of understanding and complete inability to tolerate frustration, it is really as if his mother had died. He does not know death, but only absence; and if the only person who can satisfy his imperative need is absent, she might as well be dead, so overwhelming is his sense of loss." [9]

Every human being is extremely sensitive to the departure of important people in his or her life. For many this parting is the beginning of one of life's most unbearable traumas—especially when it happens during the early years of life. The twenty-four-hour fetal contact with the mother cannot be maintained after birth, and in normal child development this contact is broken at exactly the right moment with the right duration and with the backing of a great amount of love. Caring mothers know instinctively just when and how to do this, and in so doing, they lay a correct foundation for the emotional development of the child.

The importance of this "parting reaction" has initiated much research within medical circles because there are indications that an incomplete contact development between mother and child can result in psychiatric problems and psychosomatic ailments. This "parting reaction" leads in reality to a bereavement problem—one of the earliest of these problems in a human's life, but certainly not the last. And these parting reactions have to be handled effectively from the very first one on, in order to live a healthy, well-adjusted life.

In 1967, the *Journal of Psychosomatic Research* published an article written by two eminent researchers, Dr. T. H. Holmes and Dr. R. H. Rahe, that is still being used today whenever graduate students in psychology are asked to study the relationship between excessive stress and the onset of psychosomatic illness.[10]

The article discussed the method, developed by Holmes and Rahe, to evaluate the everyday "crisis value" of all major life experiences. To do this they have formulated their findings in what they aptly call "Life Crisis Units." These Life Crisis Units were conceived from forty-three different life events and given a Life Crisis Unit rating according to the severity of the event.

Their "Social Readjustment Rating Scale" looks like this:

Rank	Life Event	Mean Value of Life Crisis Units
1	Death of a spouse	100
2	Divorce	73
3	Marital separation	65
4	Jail term	63
5	Death of a close family member	63
6	Personal injury or illness	53
7	Marriage	50
8	Fired at work	47
9	Marital reconciliation	45
10	Retirement	45
11	Change in health of family member	44
12	Pregnancy	40
13	Sex difficulties	39
14	Gain of new family member	39
15	Business readjustment	39
16	Change of financial state	38
17	Death of a close friend	37
18	Change to different line of work	36
19	Change in number of arguments with spouse	35
20	Mortgage over $10,000	31
21	Foreclosure of mortgage or loan	30
22	Change in responsibilities at work	29
23	Son or daughter leaving home	29
24	Trouble with in-laws	29
25	Outstanding personal achievement	28
26	Wife begins or stops work	26
27	Begin or end school	26
28	Change in living conditions	25
29	Revision of personal habits	24
30	Trouble with boss	23
31	Change in work hours or conditions	20
32	Change in residence	20
33	Change in school	20

Rank	Life Event	Mean Value of Life Crisis Units
34	Change in recreation	19
35	Change in church activities	19
36	Change in social activities	18
37	Mortgage or loan less than $10,000	17
38	Change in sleeping habits	16
39	Change in number of family get-togethers	15
40	Change in eating habits	15
41	Vacation	13
42	Christmas	12
43	Minor violations of the law	11

Some of the life events on the original 1967 scale probably should be modified to reflect the change in values and lifestyle we have experienced during the past fourteen years. Life event No. 3, for example, should be worded so that couples living together, yet not married, should be included. The mortgage over $10,000 might have been a stressful point to some people in 1967, but considering that the average mortgage interest rate has changed from 4.5 percent to 13 percent since that time, the value of this event might have climbed considerably. Also, No. 26 should now probably read, "Spouse begins or stops work," while the minor stress experienced during the sad moments of reflection during Christmas or the guilt feelings for getting caught speeding, or parking in a nonparking zone should also be modified to reflect current conditions and changes in the law.

In any case, most of their scale is still correct. *Over a period of two years*, a person who accumulates a total of 0–149 Life Crisis Units is not expected to have any significant psychosomatic problems within the foreseeable future.

A rating of 150–199 means a "mild life crisis" with a 33 percent rating of a psychosomatic disturbance. Next comes a rating of 200–299, termed a "moderate life crisis," with a 50 percent chance of psychosomatic illness, while a rating of 300 or more carries with it an illness probability of 80 percent! "Death of a spouse" alone rates a full 100 Life Crisis Units in the Social Readjustment Rating Scale!

The physical or emotional disturbance that results from a Life Crisis Unit accumulation may be short-lived and may therefore be relatively harmless. When, however, the stressful reaction is prolonged and extreme, it can result in an increased chance of illness, and even death.

Figures compiled by Dr. Beverley Raphael of the Health Commission of New South Wales, Australia, show that because of the increase in stress, the expected rate of death for a surviving spouse may be ten times the normal rate in the year following the year of the bereavement, or five times the expected rate for other close relatives. Also, in cases where a loved one has died from illness, accident, or suicide, the survivor is subject to terminal cardiovascular disease. If the original death occurred away from home—in a hospital or in a traffic accident, for example—then the risk of death for the survivors may increase another two to five times!

Dr. Raphael also reports a substantially increased morbidity. Her findings show that up to 43 percent of widows admit to a general health impairment in the year following the husband's death. This coincides with an increased utilization of medical services with a whopping 240 percent increase for depression and psychiatric symptoms for those under age sixty-five, and a significant increase in somatic symptoms for those over sixty-five. Also, psychological symptoms, gastro-intestinal pain and headaches are increased in at least one third of the widows in the first thirteen months following the husband's death.

But there is more.

Psychosomatic diseases such as ulcerative colitis, asthma, leukemia, hyperthyroidism, and osteo-arthritis have also been diagnosed. To top it off, there is also an increase of up to 76 percent of psychiatric symptoms, especially depression, general nervousness, fear of a nervous breakdown and insomnia, often combined with a sharply increased intake of sedatives, tranquilizers and alcohol.[11]

It is not known to which extent bereavement has affected social morbidity, although 75 percent of widows in one survey reported social withdrawal and loneliness and a 47 percent decrease in capacity to work.[12]

It is no wonder, therefore, that "death of a spouse" on the Holmes and Rahe Social Readjustment Rating Scale should rate a full 100 Life Crisis Units, for whereas a normal, relatively uneventful life can easily accumulate 200 Life Crisis Units within a two-year period, carrying with it a 50 percent chance of getting close to a psychosomatic illness, the single fact that the "death of a spouse" can push it to the breaking point of mental and physical endurance by adding another 100 units to the scale can create havoc in a human life, for it increases the chances of illness to 80 percent!

This does not leave much of a chance for leading a normal life, unless the threatening crisis can be quickly resolved and brought back to within reasonable limits of endurance. It is this limit that should not be violated. Certainly in everyone's life there are numerous losses that need to be dealt with in order to continue existing within a reasonable degree of normalcy, but it is our individual approach to these losses that will ultimately help determine our future.

Bereavement, the painful reaction to a loss, is a crisis experience that in the acute stages lasts up to three or four months. It is a life crisis situation that may precipitate a period of severe stress to the human body. Loss of a loved one is one of the most intensely painful experiences any human being can suffer. And not only is it painful to experience, but it is also painful to witness, if only because we are so impotent to help. To the bereaved nothing but the return of the lost person can bring true comfort; should what we provide fall short of that, it is felt almost as an insult.[13]

When the feeling of utter loss is the result of the death of a close friend or a relative, then a bereavement process of such intensity can begin that it may be difficult to believe that you are not the only one who is experiencing such a major sadness. In fact, the intensity of the feelings in a major bereavement often frightens people, both those experiencing it and those who stand helplessly on the sidelines watching a loved one grope his or her way blindly through the tortures of hell. It is not uncommon for someone consumed by grief to lose control of his or her feelings for a time, bursting into tears at the most inopportune moments, or becoming excessively irritable for no apparent reason. It has been described by patients as "a feeling of cascading confusion, bordering on the ragged edge of insanity." Hallucinations, seeing the missing person in a rushing crowd or on a busy street, or hearing the loved one's voice call out the name of the bereaved, often adds to the already devastating feelings of loss and dejection.

Commenting on a bereavement, Sigmund Freud once expressed his feelings in a way that needs no explanation or comment.

"Although we know that after such a loss the acute state of mourning will subside," he wrote to a friend, "we also know we shall remain inconsolable and will never find a substitute. No matter what may fill the gap, even if it is filled completely, it nevertheless remains something else. And, actually, this is how it should be, it is the only way of perpetuating that love which we do not want to relinquish."[14]

We have seen people accept a loss as a matter-of-fact occurrence; others will appear surprised but they too will shrug their shoulders and save their grief for another day. Most individuals, however, suffer shock as a first reaction, a numbness that leaves them feeling absolutely nothing or feeling simply unreal. They're there—and yet they're not. They hear the voices of their friends around them and see their faces, but the bereaved person does not react in any way. He or she has turned cold and apparently indifferent. Especially if the loss is caused by the breaking of a close relationship such as the death of a husband, a wife, a lover or a child, and it has cut deeply into a bond that was good, wholesome and satisfying in every sense of the word, then the sudden loss has made the world collapse.

Often the shock is so overwhelming that when they do see and hear what is happening around them, they still don't *feel*, and this experience can last for days. It may begin to gnaw and cause a sense of guilt because they know they should at least feel something, and yet they don't. Then, without warning, the already confused mind becomes invaded by sudden waves of almost physical pain, feelings of desolation, of aloneness and despair, mixed with an almost indescribable measure of anxiety about what has happened and what will still happen—and superimposed on it all is often a feeling of guilt for something one did or did not do.

A mother who lost her two-year-old child due to a sudden illness expressed her indifference, desolation and despair in a letter that betrays her innermost reactions.

Writing about the final moments before the death of her child, she wrote:

"Suddenly the doctors came into the room and began to watch the apparatus. I realized that something was going to happen and I began to watch too. Suddenly I noticed a change in the graph that was displayed on the glass of the oscilloscope. Someone said that it would be all right if I held D. for a moment. I don't know whether I did it or not. I don't think I did. Then they asked us to wait in another room so they could wash D. I thought, 'They're going to stuff him full of cotton!' In the waiting room there were a lot of people who began to embrace me; they cried, and they said things, and I began to wonder what they were doing there. I didn't like it and began to see them from a distance. . . . There was a man who asked for permission for an autopsy, and someone said that I had to do it, so I said yes, after which the man gave me the guarantee that we wouldn't see a bit of it.

"In the days that followed I lived in total amazement.

I spent most of the days eating, drinking, laughing, crying and making love, and all of it in tremendous amounts. Often I laid down on D.'s bed and smelled his odor, and told myself, 'He's dead, he's dead . . . ,' and waited for the sorrow to hit me, but it never did. I wanted to see him every day because I didn't understand. When I cried, I didn't cry from sorrow but because I didn't understand all the strange things that were happening. He simply laid there with his orange hair, and he was so very cold, and it fascinated me to hear how they had taken him out of the icebox. I had never seen a cremation and the surprises came one after the other. To me it was a play and I was the public. . . . I saw the coffin go down into the floor, and I thought, 'This is not real. This is a joke!' And I had to control myself before I'd burst out laughing. . . ."[15]

Confusion can indeed be a major ingredient of the bereavement process, for the feelings go so deep that their contact with reality becomes a feeble thread. The relationship between the mourner and the deceased has, of course, much to do with it. If the relationship with the dead person was mixed with love and hate, then there are often feelings of relief at being free, and this in itself can cause severe guilt.

But how about anger?

Don't think that won't enter into it, for it does in a large measure, and it is often directed at those closely associated with the deceased, at friends, at relatives, possibly God and, finally, at the dead person for having left his or her loved one, for openly deserting!

Remember, grievers are not acting rationally. They are confused and strike out at anyone in their distress. The frequently recurring questions, "Why did it happen?" or "Why me?," unanswerable as they are, keep echoing through the mind and throb with painful monotony, prolonging the grief.

Grievers often show these symptoms at the most inopportune

moments, crying out for answers while their questions are in reality only bits and flashes of distorted emotion. But these waves of feelings gradually become less frequent and less intense, only to return in force at times like Christmas and birthdays and on the anniversary of the death. These reactions take various forms such as the appearance of symptoms the lost person had in his last illness, or a recurrence of the feelings the mourner himself underwent at the time of the loss. Reactions such as these may occur either at the anniversary of the death, or when the mourner reaches the age at which the lost person died.[16]

Fortunately, people differ in the length of time necessary to "let go" of the dead person and reorganize their lives. Grief usually reaches its peak within three or four months after the bereavement and 85 percent of the bereaved are relatively symptom free by the end of the first year.[17] But even though this difference exists, it does not mean that there is perhaps a shortcut or escape from this process of recovery. *There is not.* It is a normal thing that must take place—that will take place. This is the price we must pay for being attached to someone. In fact, in the recovery process, we may safely talk about grief work that *must* be done in order to become whole again.

There simply is no escape possible.

There is no other way.

An entirely new behavior pattern has to be created by the bereaved, his family, friends and acquaintances in order to help him or her find the most appropriate way of strengthening these beginnings of a new existence. Important as this new existence is for adults, its significance in the emotional development of children may be even greater. Childhood bereavement may interfere substantially with personality development and lead to the later development of psychiatric illnesses such as severe depression and mental disturbances that can lead to suicide.

What causes a crisis for one person, however, may not have the same effect on another person.

The breakup of a relationship, the end of a love affair, the dissolution of a marriage, the loss of a home, job or money, or even moving away from a neighborhood where one has lived for a great number of years may constitute a loss that can actually result in a grief situation that will seem insurmountable. Also, a crisis can occur in the areas of human development and maturation, such as adolescence, the beginning of school, graduation, engagement, marriage, choice of occupation, parenthood, retirement, surgery, etc. Of particular interest in this latter area are the losses of parts of the body because of accidents, or sudden inability to work because of illness.

Each in its own way, these crises can lead to an emotional instability that can contain all the elements of a classic bereavement. Also, these crises must be worked through and resolved, or physical, psychological and social impairment may result from the bereavement with an intensity that is far beyond what should be expected.

The consequences of unresolved stress are pointed out by J. R. Hodge in an article in the *Journal of Religion and Health*, where he writes:

"The problem must be brought into the open and confronted no matter how unpleasant it may be for the patient. There is no healthy escape from this. *The grief work must be done.* We might even add that *the grief work will be done.* Sooner or later, correctly or incorrectly, completely or incompletely, in a clear or distorted manner, *it will be done.* People have a natural tendency to avoid the unpleasantness of the grief work, but it is necessary, and the more actively it is done the shorter will be the period of grief. If the grief work is not actively pursued, the process may be fixated or absorbed or delayed, with the patient feeling that he may have escaped it. However, almost certainly a distorted form of the grief work will appear at some time in the future." [18]

A great deal has been written during the last decade about grief reactions and the treatment of grief, but it has practically always dealt with the treatment of grief *during* and *surrounding* the moment of death. In our society, we have always shied away from death—as if that makes it go away. We don't want to face the reality of death. We even make our corpses look alive through a masterful application of makeup, hoping that by applying this façade we are helping the relatives pass through a difficult period in their lives. But grief does not limit itself to the period surrounding a tragic and stressful event; its menacing tentacles can reach far beyond the expected boundaries of sorrow and penetrate into what could have been healthy, productive years of life.

It used to be that with the end of life and the entry of the mortician, the survivors had to find their own way out of their emotional dilemma. The commercially acquired sympathy extended by the undertaker, and the sincere sorrow shown by close relatives extended only so far and no farther. There were boundaries to the mourning period, and even though they were not clearly defined in most Western societies, once the mourning period had passed, the closest survivors were "on their own."

The recognition of the power of death and its undeniable influence on the life expectancies and health of the closest surviving relatives is beginning to change all that. Being "on their own" isn't all that simple. Death is a fact of life, and the sooner we recognize this harsh reality, the better we can prepare for the entry of this savage intruder.

A distinction must be made between the two major types of bereavement—*normal bereavement* and *pathological bereavement*. Someone has a normal bereavement when he or she manages to work through a personal reaction and reconstruct everyday life without additional crisis. This reaction/reconstruction usually involves a brief period of shock, numbness and disbelief, followed by intense emotions associated with the loss. During this time the bereaved is engulfed in feelings of pining and yearning, and filled with anguish, protests what has happened. The bereaved repeatedly asks himself, "Why this time?," "Why this one?," but of course there are no answers. Death is not only a "fact of life" but also a *"risk of life,"* and we have to learn to live with it.

As the days go by, the reality of death sinks in and during the weeks following the initial shock, sadness, despair and hopelessness dominate the emotional life of the survivor. The very idea that life must go on—but this time without the deceased—makes everything seem useless and without meaning. It is at this time, too, that the bereaved is totally preoccupied with memories of the deceased and finds the need to review these memories frequently and give expression to them in talks with close friends, not wanting to close the door to the past, but hang on. . . .

This review of the lost relationship is a vital psychological aspect of the mourning process and, if this process is not worked through satisfactorily, the loss cannot be resolved.

If there is a place for angry feelings, perhaps in terms of the many needs that will now be unfulfilled, or feelings that will center on the futility of the untimely death, then *this* is the time when anger will appear.[19] But, as with all other emotional aspects of grief, it is essential for the bereaved person to be able to express these feelings of anger and come to terms with them in order to resolve the loss.

But under normal conditions, this phase also passes, and slowly the individual will begin to direct his attention to his surroundings, and the outside world will once again become meaningful to him.

The period of mourning is ended.

Life begins anew.

Most people are able to handle their losses in their own way and will work through the entire process without too much of an emotional problem. They will find their place among the 85 percent who managed without outside help. But not everyone reacts identically, and the computers' memory banks are filled with the case histories of those whose sorrow has never been resolved

and who have drifted over into what has become known as
pathological bereavement.

Research conducted at the Department of Psychiatry at Sydney University in Australia has revealed several patterns of pathological grieving associated with problems following bereavement and the increased risk of health impairment. The very term "pathological bereavement" implies that the bereavement process has not progressed along satisfactory lines and furthermore has not been of the right intensity. The drifting over into the area of "stunted bereavement" is different for each individual. There is no standard time for each person because everyone has his or her own way of processing sorrow. Those who do not show any reaction whatsoever to a loss and who deny themselves the "luxury" of grief, together with those individuals whose reaction is so pathological to start with that nothing *but* a psychiatric illness can be expected, are the potential patients.

Following the fire that swept through the Cocoanut Grove nightclub in Boston on November 28, 1942, in which 491 people were killed, several studies were conducted aimed at identifying the various grief components that could be considered as typical or atypical of a normal grief reaction. One of the reports describes the stages of normal grief as a process involving

- initial shock
- intense sadness
- withdrawal from the environment
- protest of the loss
- a gradual resolution of the loss.

The same study, however, also identified a number of characteristics that were considered abnormal grief reactions. These were
- somatic distress
- preoccupation with the deceased
- feelings of guilt

- loss of warmth in relationship with other people
- a disorganized pattern of conduct.[20]

This "preoccupation with the deceased" often manifests itself in a "chronic search" for the deceased, often accompanied by hallucinations. This, however, is not a phenomenon that is typical only of the pathologically bereaved; it is fairly typical with all the bereaved and is considered to be one of the most frequently encountered symptoms of bereavement. It is sometimes expressed in an almost uncontrollable urge to drift away from home, always searching, always yearning for the deceased but never finding fulfillment. Others just stay at home and spend their time at the place where the deceased felt most at ease, and they can't be moved to another location. In cases where a move has taken place, many experience such a deeply felt feeling of homesickness that it becomes apparent that the deceased is still very much a controlling part of their existence.

The second reaction, the hallucinatory phenomenon, usually centers on a deeply-rooted attempt to recall the deceased in fantasy. A systematic research program dealing with reactions of this sort has shown that this "holding on" to the deceased occurs much more frequently than was otherwise thought possible.

A detailed study, conducted by Dr. W. D. Rees, a British physician,[21] covering patients in his own practice and that of two of his colleagues, centered on the occurrence of hallucinations among widows—a phenomenon that is not as uncommon as often thought, especially not in people who are placed in a situation of severe emotional stress. Both auditory hallucinations (involving the sense of hearing) and visual hallucinations (involving the sense of sight) are part of this phenomenon. It is not unusual for a mourner to see the deceased sitting in his or her favorite chair, standing in the doorway, or taking part in some familiar activity. These hallucinations are often experienced as the result of a feeling of intense guilt or anxiety.

Martin Luther once had such a strong anxiety-related hallucination of the Devil that he threw an inkwell at the apparition.

A young woman who felt very guilty about the death of her son was more surprised than sad and wrote:

> "I tried to act the way it was expected of me, and the feeling that I never really loved him became stronger and stronger, together with the idea that I really didn't mind the fact that he had died. I began to believe that he had died just because of that; that he had always been unhappy and finally committed suicide. . . .
>
> "I felt the need to compensate for the absence of sorrow. Through the creation of my own religion in which I played the role of priestess, I felt myself far above the people with their "common" grief. My son was the God, and because I felt guilty about his death, he gave me signs and instructions to follow.
>
> "The first one of these I received through a vision.
>
> "I was laying in bed and looked out through the window. It was storming and the limbs of the trees combined with the wind to create a terrible noise. Suddenly I saw his face in the tree top, and from the manner in which he looked at me I knew that he needed me. There was a way to get to him. I cut my wrists and while the blood poured out of me, I drifted upward toward him. It was a clear command. I had to cut my wrists and then we would be united again."

This case is certainly out of the ordinary and should not be regarded as a typical hallucination in a case of bereavement, yet it does show that the hallucinations can range all the way from seeing the deceased standing innocently in the doorway to one that may result in an attempt at self-destruction.

On testing the patient with the Minnesota Multiphasic Personality Inventory (MMPI) test, one of the leading personality tests in use today, she scored extremely high on both the psychotic and neurotic scale and was in dire need of professional help.

The Rees study discovered that among the widows eligible for the survey, 50 percent experienced hallucinations during the first few months following the death of their husband—but few of them dared to talk about it. Bad marriages resulted in few or no hallucinations, but where there had been happy and highly successful marriages, hallucinations were regular occurrences.

Among the reasons given for not sharing their imaginary experiences with others, 14 percent of the widows indicated that they did not want to be regarded as "odd"; 40 percent of them admitted to having been in physical touch with the hallucinations; 14 percent had only visual hallucinations; another 14 percent actually *heard* him speak. What's more, 12 percent of the widows polled admitted to speaking with their husbands on a regular basis—to them sufficient reason to avoid mentioning it!

Let's look at it this way.

We all experience losses throughout our lives, whether these losses entail the death of a loved one or the separation from objects dear to us. We may shrug off these losses as expected occurrences, or retreat into a deep depression because of them. We may or may not resolve the problem, but one thing is certain: The emotional experience that accompanies the "loss" is firmly encoded in our minds and cannot be erased. Each individual determines the nature of this coded impression, and it varies from person to person, but it is nevertheless an influencing factor in the development of one's emotional life. The strength of this coded message that finds its way into our memory bank depends on the value we place on unity and completeness. Here too, we are all different, with one individual being able to bear much more emotional trauma than another.

How much can we afford to lose before we begin to get the feeling that we are really missing something? That we are no longer a complete unit?

This is indeed one of the central issues underlying the intensity of the trauma that results from a loss. There is no doubt that the strength of this "trauma signal" and its subsequent encoding in the human memory bank bears its share of the responsibility for the depth and intensity of the grief experienced by the survivor. Sometimes it spills over into conscious behavior, and the obvious problems result.

We are social creatures, and we make attachments to people whether we like it or not. And *because* we make these attachments, we have to face unavoidable consequences when these ties are broken. But as with everything else in life, there will be new relationships and new attachments, and when these in turn run their course and are eventually severed, another period of grief may set in. This is one of the sadder truths of life. The intensity of this feeling of loss is closely tied to the replaceability of the object lost. In the case of a stolen car, the loss may generate a feeling of anger that will slowly dissipate within a week or two, but when it concerns the death of a child or a loved one, even though you may decide on another baby or find a new mate, the original can never be replaced.

Somehow things are different.

In the relationship of loss and grief, we are dealing with an unwritten natural law, for the more attached an individual is to something, the deeper the grief will be when that "something" is taken away. However, it isn't that simple. The feelings that are generated at the loss of a parent are not the same as those that accompany the death of a child. With a parent you realize that he or she is getting older, and you slowly begin to accept the idea that death for him or her will come sooner or later. This realization is the beginning of anticipatory grief. "She has already enjoyed the major portion of her life," you reason, "and her eventual death will be a natural ending."

With the child, however, life has only just begun, and when it is interrupted by sudden death it generates the feeling that this death is a real tragedy. The child has been deprived of a full life; the parent has not. Thus the "degree of attachment" has been complicated by the additional factor of "full life expectancy," making an acceptance of the loss so much more difficult.

There is little chance that any one of us will be able to avoid the experience of a loss during our lifetime. But how we respond to it, and how we react to the resulting bereavement should nevertheless be major concerns. Grief is an extremely stressful experience, and an awareness of our individual threshold of stress and emotional anguish may help us withstand the complications of a bereavement.

CHAPTER TWO

The Boundaries of Physical Endurance

Go home, dear friends
Lament no more
I'm not lost
Merely gone before
My earthly parents loved me well
So much that language fails to tell
But oh, their love was weak and poor
My heavenly Father loves me more.[1]

THROUGHOUT HISTORY, the side effects of death, grief and mourning have been known to produce significant bodily changes in the bereaved. The prophet Isaiah, in biblical times, admonished his fellow Israelites to "bind up the brokenhearted," and the literature of other cultures and eras also makes continual references to the physical effects of grief.

Take this from our own society.

There are about thirty million married Americans aged fifty and older. Each year about seven hundred thousand of them lose a spouse,[2] and there is an elevated risk of death among these bereaved, especially among the men. This elevated risk is partially due to social isolation and the difficulties encountered by men in making the necessary lifestyle adjustments, thereby making them more vulnerable to other stresses. In fact, the risk of mortality may actually be as high as 50 percent in persons suffering a bereavement caused by the death of a spouse—a common event in persons over fifty.[3] And, although younger widows are fewer in absolute numbers, the risks for them are even greater than for men.

These bereavement reactions, however, are not limited to those people who suffered "loss by death." The psychologist A. Schmale [4] revealed that 98 percent of the patients admitted to a general hospital experienced loss of someone or something —which was accompanied by feelings of helplessness and hopelessness—prior to the onset of their disease. One of the interesting aspects of this study was that the definition of "loss" had been kept very broad and included actual loss, actual threat of loss, and symbolic loss of a valued possession. In the actual loss category, loss of a "valued possession" was experienced by 12 percent of the patients. These losses were quite varied and included the death of a sibling, marital separation, broken engagements, and loss of a valuable object. In the area of actual threat, 21 percent could be ranked, as they had experienced a change in health, a negative change in the behavior of someone close to them, etc. A symbolic loss of an object, such as failing grades, friends forgetting a date, etc., was experienced by 38 percent, and 29 percent of the group of patients reported no loss at all, although the investigator was able to make an interpretation of actual threatened or symbolic loss for eleven out of twelve patients.

The interval between the final feelings of hopelessness and helplessness and the onset of the disease was within twenty-five hours for 38 percent of the patients, and within one week for 36 percent. And, even though the patients suffered from a very diverse group of illnesses, the majority of them were cardiovascular (17 percent), diseases of the nervous system (17 percent), digestive diseases (12 percent), and respiratory problems (12 percent). This study uncovered a direct connection between the diseases and feelings of "helplessness and hopelessness" in these hospitalized patients. Although considerable research is being done in this area, the actual causal relationship between hopelessness and helplessness on one hand and disease on the other is not known. The disease may cause these feelings, but the feelings of hopelessness and helplessness may also have a direct bearing on the development of the disease.

As early as 1959, a number of alarming indications emerged as the result of a study initiated and conducted by A. S. Kraus and A. M. Lilienfeld; yet much of their findings remain unused, on dusty library shelves.[5]

Let's take a look at exactly what they did and at the frightening results.

These researchers calculated the mortality rates for widows and widowers by matching data taken from the National Office of Vital Statistics for the year 1956 with information they received from the 1950 Census.

The death rates of widowed subjects were compared to the rates for married men and women matched for age, race and sex. A careful comparison indicated that the death rate for white widowers aged twenty-five to thirty-four was 4.3 times greater than the death rate for white males of the same age! For nonwhite widowers aged twenty-five to thirty-four, the mortality rate was 3.9 times greater than their married controls. White widows aged twenty-four to thirty-four had a mortality rate 2.7 times greater than white married females, and nonwhite widows of the same age showed a mortality rate 2.8 times greater than their controls. Specifically, the younger widows and widowers (aged twenty to twenty-four and twenty-five to thirty-four) had the highest ratio of mortality for eight causes of death as compared to the young married group!

For all of the diseases combined the mortality was at least seven times greater among the young widowed people (under age forty-five) than for the matched young married control group. The young male widowers appeared to be especially at "high risk" for death from cardiovascular disease, with which their mortality rate was ten times higher than that for the married men of their age. The researchers concluded that as a group the recently bereaved were "greater at risk" for mortality![6]

Five years later, some of the results obtained gained additional strength from research conducted in England that showed that the mortality rate among widowed women was higher during the six-month period after initial bereavement than at any other time during the five-year follow-up period. In fact, a similar study conducted among American males had similar results, and stated emphatically that "during the first six months after bereavement, the mortality rate among the widowers rose 40 percent as compared to the expected mortality rate among the married men of the same age." [7]

Many more studies have been conducted since that time, and all point in the same dreaded direction—that there *is* a connection between grief due to loss and a higher death rate. This conclusion rests on cold, hard, statistical facts. Even when we take all the biasing factors that are present in every study into account, we still have to admit that the recently bereaved have a greater chance of contracting a life-threatening disease than those who have not been exposed to a process of loss.

The question is: Why?

We really don't know enough about the human body to be able to arrive at an adequate answer, but today scientists in the field of psychology and medicine are examining a number of possible causes.

The first possibility is that "the unfit tend to marry the unfit." This idea has no value since most causes of mortality associated with the bereavement are usually not present at the ages of courtship and marriage, but develop in later years. Of course, there is always the possibility that two people with a susceptibility to the same illness may end up marrying one another, but this chance happening does not occur often enough to lend sufficient weight to this assumption.

A second possibility is that the spouses have been exposed to the same unfavorable environment at the same time. Individuals who become widowed have indeed shared influences that may have contributed to the death of the spouse. There may be poor sanitation, unbalanced nutrition, poor housing, or a high degree of social stress and other factors. That these influences do exist is undeniable, but the degree to which they contribute to the problem is unknown.

The "effects of widowhood" are a third possibility. The

events surrounding the bereavement and the attempt to adjust to the subsequent conditions of widowhood have deleterious effects that manifest themselves in an excessive death rate. The adjustment to widowhood can be extremely stressful—depending on the individual. It may include the sorrow and agony that results from the loss, combined with the uncertainty that comes with the responsibility of a single life, changes in diet, work schedule and recreational life, a reduced income and the modifications in economic conditions and lifestyle.

Another possibility involves the "loss of care" that is closely related to the effects of widowhood. The widowed are forced to adapt to a different way of living. A survivor may neglect early evidence of a developing disease, as in failing to seek help for cancer when obvious signs of the onset of the disease are detected. Also, the management of chronic diseases such as hypertension and diabetes may be neglected, and because of the disorganization and hurt that has followed the loss, the survivor may turn to an excessive use of alcohol, thereby increasing the risk for cirrhosis and accidents. Also, because alcohol abuse has a self-destructive element, it may aggravate depression, thereby increasing the possibility of suicide. The deceased may also have been the medically responsible one in the marriage, and his or her absence may add to the total physical neglect.[8]

The final possibility is the "desolation effect."[9] This effect centers on the loneliness and the aloneness experienced by many who have experienced a bereavement. The "effects of widowhood" may mean a drastic change in schedule and activities as well as economic conditions, but the "desolation effect" includes none of these. It has also been referred to as "desolate pining," an existence wherein the memory of the loss controls all actions, and nothing matters but reminiscing, dreaming, remembering, and a total surrender to the trauma of the loss.

The "effects of widowhood" and the "desolation effect" are the two most logical causes of contracting life-threatening disease and have become the focal points of grief investigations, for they have directed the attention of medical and social-science researchers to the psychobiological effects of grief.

In our society, we are eager to try to connect disease with infection, heredity, pollution and a variety of other possible influences on the human body. The idea that bereavement or "pathological grief" caused by a variety of factors—not merely by the death of a loved one—can be a vital contributing factor to the increase in morbidity and mortality has begun to erode this idea because of the undeniable results of research programs that have provided us with evidence that a number of killer diseases, the most important being cancer, can be linked to bereavement and grief.

Gerald L. Klerman, professor of psychiatry, and Judith E. Izen, research analyst at Harvard Medical School and Psychiatric Service and Massachusetts General Hospital in Boston, Massachusetts, focused attention on this area in a report in 1977 in which they compiled some of the pertinent facts about this newly discovered link.

One study showed that when death occurred due to the abnormal new growth of tissue (cancer), 72 percent of adult cancer patients had experienced a significant psychic loss (loss of a meaningful person or job, or a role change) within six months to nine years prior to the onset of the growth, as compared to loss of 10 percent among healthy people in a control group.[10] Another study revealed that the death rate for malignant growths doubled among the bereaved of all age groups and sexes compared to the death rates due to cancerous growths among married patients in the control group.[11] Still another research project conducted on the background of patients suffering from breast cancer [12] has produced results indicating that 22 percent—nine out of forty women—had experienced a death of an important person in their lives within two years of the onset of cancer, while 50 percent or twenty women from the same group reported increasing feelings of guilt in the twelve months preceding the discovery of the cancer. This feeling was experienced simultaneously with bouts of depression, anxiety, self-criticism and self-condemnation.[13] While these findings are undoubtedly of interest to the female population, it may come as a welcome surprise to them that a study conducted in 1959 by Kraus and Lilienfeld found no significant difference between widows and married women in the death rate as the result of breast cancer! [14]

The findings mentioned above are in some ways supported by statistics that were compiled from patients suffering from cancer of the cervix. This cancer site has been studied to test the theory that among women external loss would be manifested in female organ changes. Indeed, one project did discover a high ratio of cancer of the genital organs in widowed females as compared to their married controls.[15] In another evaluation F. P. Paloucek and J. B. Graham studied eighty-eight consecutive patients [16] and discovered that 65 percent of women suffering from cancer of the ovary, uterus and cervix admitted to having undergone a recent "debilitating" experience. This "debilitating experience" was later defined as either a physical illness, such as a respiratory infection; a psychological change, such as the death of a husband; or a combined physical and psychosocial change, such as a patient caring for a mother who had suffered a stroke.[17]

It was only a matter of time before someone would test these findings in an original and different way—and it was left to two eminent researchers, Dr. A. Schmale and Dr. H. Iker, to initiate and develop a drastically new program, one of the first to separate the occurrence of actual loss due to death from feelings of helplessness and hopelessness. Their study was aimed at assessing the psychological state of the patient manifesting a somatic disease to determine whether the person had actually undergone a grieving process.[18]

Next, employing different methods than previously used, they found that among a group of fifty-one women who had entered a hospital for biopsies, psychiatrists were actually able to forecast which women would have cancer and which would not. Their judgment was based on the women's responses to an open-ended interview with emphasis on admissions of feelings of helplessness or hopelessness during the six months prior to the biopsy. The resulting predictions of cancer were statistically significant. *They actually anticipated a diagnosis of cancer in eleven cases.* They reported that the occurrence of the death of a loved one was equal among both groups: one loss among the nineteen women with uterine cancer as compared to one loss among the thirty-two women who had nonmalignant biopsies.[19]

Other dreaded forms of cancer—leukemia and lymphoma—have also been singled out as targets for cancer stress-related research programs, and the results are equally as alarming for both men and women. Based upon a study that investigated the role of loss and separation among patients with leukemia and lymphoma in 1954, Dr. W. Greene reported that 85 percent of men admitted to the hospital with a diagnosis of leukemia or lymphoma—and he was referring to seventeen out of twenty patients between the ages of twenty-five and seventy-seven, with an average age of forty-nine—had experienced loss or separation from a mother figure, either their wife or mother. At the same time, they were also reporting other psychic losses because of retirement, injury, or change of work. The weakness in this report, however, is that it does not state the time that elapsed between the occurrence of the various losses and the onset of the leukemia or lymphoma.[20]

Other projects set up by Dr. Greene resulted in a report covering the results of a study conducted on thirty-two women aged twenty to seventy-one who had been admitted to the hospital with a diagnosis of leukemia or lymphoma. *A surprising 75 percent of these women had undergone significant losses prior to their hospitalization.* Other findings resulting from additional research studies by Dr. Greene are even more devastating in their predictive value. For example, of a group of sixty-one men between the ages of twenty-one and eighty-five, 51 percent reported that they had experienced recent loss or separation from important people in their lives within four years of the onset of their leukemia or lymphoma. Fourteen men out of the group (23 percent) had experienced loss of a mother, five of them (8 percent) had lost a father, and twelve of the men (20 percent) had lost a wife. To complicate it more, twenty-seven of the men (44 percent) were trying to adjust to a threatened disability from an operation they had yet to undergo. Also, nineteen of the group (31 percent) had lost a job and 34 percent of them had recently retired. The men may have developed the onset of the disease in a situation in which they were exposed to loss of personal and emotional support from either their mother or a "mother figure"—that is, any person who either has taken the place of a mother or who cares for an individual with the feelings or qualities characteristic of a mother.

For those of us who regard cancer as a disease that might have environmental or dietary causes, the realization that our everyday way of life carries a good share of the responsibility for the steadily increasing rate of cancer may come as a shock—yet the indications are there. What remains now is to identify the processes responsible for transforming stress into cancer, and research in this area is continually progressing.

Beginning more than a decade ago, in 1969, a number of investigators began to speculate about biological mechanisms that would intervene between bereavement and the growth and dissemination of cancerous cells. The research has continued ever since.

Underlying this research are some basic facts that are undeniable. It is known, for example, that various immunological reactions of the body that recognize and destroy abnormal cells —possibly including cells undergoing cancerous transformation— are *depressed* by corticosteroid hormones. As long as the body has just the right supply of these hormones, the "search-and-destroy system" of the human organism will function adequately: It will kill the cancer cells that have invaded our bodies. One important effect of stress, however, is that it will force the body system to produce an *excess* of corticosteroids, and when that happens, the activity of the immunological processes of the body will be forced to take a less active role in the fight against malignancy, giving the cancerous process a chance to proceed practically unhindered. A grieving person, therefore, might be more susceptible to the malignant transformation of virus than a person not experiencing grief or other stress.[21] Yet, few proponents of the psychosomatic point of view would hold that stress is the single cause of cancer. Other factors such as diet or lifestyle may also share the responsibility. At best, the intense sorrow caused by loss and the bereavement and grief are precipitants causing abnormal tissue growth in individuals predisposed by genetic, immunological, viral and other conditions.

The deteriorating health of the ex-Shah of Iran is a classic example of the connection between stress and cancer. His health problems increased as the political struggle in his country began to worsen for him. His first cancer operation was performed amid seething internal unrest, and while his country rocked violently from the uncontrollable religious revolt, he went back into the hospital for additional cancer treatment.

For a while it seemed as though his battle against ill health was won, but his worries increased as the American diplomatic hostages taken by the new revolutionary regime became a pawn in the Revolutionary Council's demand for his return to Iran to stand trial. A move to Panama was soon followed by new demands for extradition, increasing the emotional stress on the Shah even more. A planned cancer operation was postponed at the last moment to make it possible for him to escape once more —this time to Cairo for both permanent exile and further cancer treatment. It was of no avail. He died a mere four months later.

If cancer is the most dreaded disease in our Western culture, cardiovascular diseases are most certainly a close second. Since Old Testament times the term "broken heart" has been used to describe someone who is bereaved. Even though this term cannot be taken as a literal description of the effects of a loss on a survivor, it has always been believed that grief does *something* to the heart—but exactly what this "something" is has always been shrouded in mystery, for no one really knew. But now the mysterious veil has been lifted, thanks to medical science, and it appears that the ancients were not all that far from the truth.

During the past ten years, a number of investigators have embarked on a piece of clever medical detective work, attempting to test the scientific validity of this piece of ancient folklore.

As sample, they took a group of 4,486 widowers aged fifty-five years and older and followed them for nine years. Through drawing careful comparisons, they discovered that the mortality rate for heart disease in the first six months of bereavement was 40 percent higher than the expected rate for the general population matched for age and sex.

But this was not all.

When other figures were added up they revealed that the death rate resulting from coronary thrombosis was a whopping 67 percent higher than expected, while the death rate from other forms of arteriosclerotic and degenerative heart disease was not less than 60 percent higher than the expected mortality rate. All this was based on national figures for Great Britain for married men of the same age! [22]

Sadly, earlier research had already found similarly high mortality rates for heart disease in a younger bereaved population for both men and women. The figures indicated that the *mortality rates due to arteriosclerotic heart disease and vascular lesions affecting the central nervous system were ten times greater among the widowed than among people in the married control group under age thirty-five.*[23] A higher mortality rate was also found among the widowed subjects for other forms of heart disease, such as chronic rheumatic heart disease, nonrheumatic chronic endocarditis and other myocardial degeneration, while hypertension with heart disease and general arteriosclerosis showed a similar pattern compared to the rates among married controls.

Dr. George Engel, psychiatrist and physician at Strong Memorial Hospital in Rochester, New York, has provided us with the most dramatic example of the effects of sudden stress on the human heart. In a research paper entitled "Sudden and Rapid Death During Psychological Stress," he confronts us with a series of 177 instances of rapid and unexpected death, 44 percent of which occurred during a period of acute grief or while the subjects were in mourning. Amazing is that the time interval between death of a "significant other" and sudden death of the individual was extremely small, varying from minutes to weeks or months. The predominant cause of death in these patients was cardiovascular disease.[24]

Diseases such as acute closed-angle glaucoma, Cushing's disease, disseminated lupus erythematosus, functional uterine bleeding, idiopathic glossodynia, pernicious anemia, pneumonia, rheumatoid arthritis, Graves' disease, tuberculosis, and ulcerative colitis have all been connected with stress in one way or another. Although the percentages of dependency on stress vary considerably from disease to disease, they all point in the same direction, blaming our hectic way of life and grief—the trauma caused by loss—as major contributory causes.[25]

Dr. Hans Selye puts it this way:

"The processes we know as worry and aging are actually nothing less than the sum total of all the scars left by the stress of life. In the medical sense, these scars are not only lines in your skin but can be chemical or mental, causing irreparable damage. Because of this the identification of the ultimate cause of stress is one of the most promising avenues of research in our time. We may be looking for a chemical substance or the lack of one—but up to now we have only theories—no facts."[26]

Where the research that is being conducted at Dr. Selye's International Institute of Stress will lead, and whether this and other projects of a similar nature will pay off in our lifetime are unknown, for the mechanism that transforms the impulses of an emotional trauma into self-destruct signals has remained totally illusive thus far. We are still dealing with a proverbial "missing link" but the search goes on.

There is, however, one thing that we do know, and that is that many of our ailments are purely psychosomatic. An over-the-counter medication or a tranquilizer from a well-meaning physician may soften the pain that betrays an inward disturbance, but the alleviation of the underlying problem can not be accomplished by a healing of the body alone.

Psychology and psychiatry have come a long way since World War II, and recent developments in therapy, of which Guided Confrontation is an excellent example, hold more promise for the healing of psychosomatic disturbances than do the miracle drugs and aspirin compounds so heavily advertised in the mass media.

CHAPTER THREE

ŤŤŤŤŤŤ

The Pathway of Grief

IT IS NEVER EASY to find an inroad into a person's world of grief and bewilderment and know exactly how to approach his or her problem. A deep emotional trauma can have many underlying causes, and the approach to a possible solution often depends on a "clinical hunch." Even though the cause of depression may not be known, we cannot shrug aside and ignore desperate pleas for help and understanding. In talking to and drawing out depressed people, we sometimes can form a feeling that an unresolved bereavement process lies as the basis of their depression—and we take it from there.

For instance, one study conducted among 135 severe "agoraphobics"—persons who fear leaving the safety of home or being in crowded places—showed that bereavement had played a major role in the onset of their problem.[1] In one urban community in England no less than 38 percent of all the women and 20 percent of all the men had a phobic disorder,[2] many of which were agoraphobic. The illness had frequently followed closely on a bereavement or a suddenly developing illness in a close relative or friend (37 percent); illness in, or an acute danger to the patient himself (31 percent); and frequently severance of family ties or acute domestic stress, which often constituted a threat to the marriage (15 percent). Thus in more than half of the cases, a bereavement process or a threat of this process was the precipitating factor for the phobia.

Bereavement plays an important role in many clinical problems and has to be considered as a possible cause for many mental disturbances. In fact, it is now considered to be such an important issue that the term "bereavement behavior" was coined in 1968 to describe the total response, both physiological and psychological, that is displayed by a person following the loss of a meaningful person, role or object.

The response pattern that follows can be divided into two elements: mourning and grief. *Mourning* refers to the conventional behavior of people as dictated by the customs of the society, while *grief* can best be defined as a stereotyped set of physiological reactions of biological origin.[3] In other words, the wearing of a black dress and a black veil or the covering of the mirrors and windows may be customary in some countries as an outward sign of mourning while weeping and other outward signs of sadness are usually regarded as typical signs of grief. In years past, social scientists attempted to cut a sharp dividing line between mourning and grief, but they have now discovered that such a demarcation line between the biological and sociocultural determinants of grief does not really exist.[4] The ritual aspects of mourning may be exhibited for purely social reasons without any of the expected affective accompaniments; grief, on the other hand, may be shown in situations where no mourning practices are prescribed. But when we get down to the real issue, mourning without grief and grief without mourning rarely occur. They are closely related components. Even though mourning as a ritual may contain little or no emotion, and grief may reveal itself devoid of the conventional trappings of mourning, they *are* usually related and in fact often complement each other.

For those who have never experienced grief, it is a difficult-to-imagine syndrome, but for one who is caught in the quicksand of its emotional torment it is an emotional upheaval that consists of one or more of the following features:

- Psychological and physiological symptoms such as withdrawal, fatigue, sleep disturbances, weeping, yearning and loss of appetite.

- The real or imagined loss of a significant object or person, which can be resolved only when a new relationship is established.
- Resistance to the establishment of new relations, which makes relief of stress all the more difficult.

And there is no denying that grief is universal. Not only does it appear among human beings all over the world, but it also can be found in other species as well, especially the higher primates. A study covering bereavement reactions in people in seventy-eight countries found that crying was the most frequent response among bereaved women.[5] Of the seventy-three countries that could be rated for crying, this response occurred in seventy-two—the Balinese of Indonesia were the only exception. Aggression—or anger—was present in fifty of fifty-six societies (89 percent). Other common reactions to bereavement were self-mutilation and fear. The researchers concluded that "at least in dim outline, the emotional responses of people in almost any culture resemble those of people in almost any other."

In order to come to an effective therapy for bereavement it is useful to have a general idea of what the grief process consists of, even though each individual case of grief is different, and the approach toward resolving the bereavement has to be modified for each individual.

Grief begins with a "stage of desolation," usually accompanied by outbursts of uncontrollable crying. If this stage has not occurred, then the whole bereavement process has been delayed or distorted. If there are also no signs of protest or aggression, then what could have been a normal bereavement process may have turned into a problem. If this coincides with the continuing search for the loved one long after his or her death, then the griever has not as yet worked through the steps or phases of the bereavement.

The stages that *must* be resolved in order to come to a resolution of grief are: *

* See the Appendix for additional information on these stages.

Phases and Components of Death Grief

Shock
Disorganization
┌ Searching Behavior
│ Emotional Components
│   Desolate Pining
│   Despair
│   Guilt
│   Anxiety
│   Jealousy
│   Shame
└   Protest, Aggression
Letting Go
Resolution and Acceptance
Reintegration

Denial

PHASES AND COMPONENTS OF DEATH GRIEF

Shock can be a momentary experience or it can be a prolonged one, lasting for a number of weeks. It has been described as a feeling of numbness, an inability to let the reality of death come through. Most people feel stunned at the moment when the news of the death hits them. "It just doesn't seem real," or "I felt it was all a dream" are typical of the remarks made. Some describe such overwhelming attacks of panic that they have to seek refuge with friends. *The duration and intensity of shock has a direct bearing on the number of difficulties incurred during the bereavement process.*

Disorganization also varies greatly from one person to the next. In this stage some people appear to be completely paralyzed, totally incapable of doing anything at all, while others operate with great efficiency and meticulously handle all the details, from filing the insurance claims and making funeral arrangements to meeting with the lawyers and disposing of the personal belongings of the deceased.

The processing of these two phases of shock and disorganization can be greatly facilitated through an effective interaction of close friends and relatives who can play a major supporting role during this time. Don't ever underestimate the value of the social network at a moment like this! Also at this point medical assistance from the family physician and competent legal advice from a trusted counselor may be of great value. This, of course, varies from case to case.

Searching behavior can range from mild restlessness without being aware of the cause, to insomnia, preoccupation with thoughts of the lost person, and quiet anticipation of the deceased's return home, to feeling his actual presence. While going through this phase, the sense of actually "feeling" his presence or "seeing" him on the street can be extremely real and very frightening. Vivid dreams during which the husband appears alive also occur, making the desolation on waking so much worse. Because these phenomena of sensing, hearing and feeling are never reinforced by the actual finding of the lost person, this phase will gradually be extinguished, even though this may take considerable time. Since many of these features are known to occur during the bereavement process of a great number of widows, there can be no doubt that this is a common feature of grief and can therefore not be considered as a phenomenon that occurs only in cases of pathological grief.

Emotional components may coincide with searching behavior. When they coincide, both tend to last longer, and inasmuch as they can appear in any order, we call them components, rather than phases. They also vary in importance and intensity for different individuals. Furthermore, they are not always present in a case of grief. Like the ocean, they ebb and flow in waves, with one following the other in quick succession. And even though their intensity may vary, they are all extremely painful.

Desolate pining has often been called by the more familiar name of depression but since that word is too broad and too all-encompassing, we prefer not to use it. The overwhelming feelings of worthlessness that are found in psychotic depressions, for example, are seldom encountered in grief. We prefer to emphasize "grief with an aspect of yearning." This is the deep, dark, empty feeling that is interspersed with crashing waves of intense psychic pain, accompanied by frequent outbursts of crying. The feeling of longing and yearning that cannot be fulfilled is often coupled with physical symptoms such as restlessness, nausea, vomiting, loss of appetite, sleep disturbances, choking sensations and various hyperventilative phenomena. Crying may seem to be uncontrollable at first, but this soon disappears, for as severe and unexpected as the outbursts may be, the griever does not really want to cause a disturbance and learns to save his or her anguish for more suitable moments when he or she is alone. If this aspect of grief is not evident during the funeral, then the stage is undoubtedly being set for emotional complications.

Societies, however, differ greatly in their reaction to death, and some deal with it by hiring paid mourners, who enter the house of the deceased to wail and cry, moaning the deceased's name over and over again until the griever finally breaks down and cries and sobs over the loss of the beloved companion. This feeling of utter hopelessness and helplessness that accompanies the loss has been termed *despair*, for while the "pining" is an active feeling that accompanies the "searching," the emotional component of despair is the dark bleakness that comes with the realization that the loss is final. Most dictionaries define "despair" as the state where one loses all hope and is overcome by a sense of futility and defeat. For his book *Death, Grief and Mourning in Contemporary Britain*, the British psychologist G. Gorer conducted a detailed study of people in a chronic state of despair and was highly surprised that in his sample of eighty patients, 10 percent were still in a state of despair. Even though the loss had occurred more than twelve months earlier, the signs were still very obvious.[6]

Guilt is also of great significance and can arise from a great variety of sources. It is not really important whether the guilt is real or imaginary, for it *has* to be dealt with. A violent quarrel just before a fatality, or the expression of "Drop dead!" occurring in an argument shortly before a death may cause just as much of a problem as being the actual cause of an accident in which a loved one is killed. The issue becomes even more complex if the relationship was an ambivalent one. In that case there is often the feeling of release from a difficult partnership, combined with the accompanying experience of feeling guilty for not being sad. In one study an attempt was made to assess the extent to which ambivalence had played a role in the marriages of a group of widows and widowers, and the questions asked dealt with issues on which most married couples are apt to disagree. When the results were tabulated, those who had reported many disagreements were doing significantly worse than those who had reported almost none.

Guilt can also arise from aggressive thoughts or feelings toward the dead; from omissions or commissions of deeds prior to the death, or for being selfishly busy with yourself and not being able to give enough attention to others.

The *anxiety* that is part of the denial phase can originate from a variety of sources and expresses itself in questions such as, "What am I going to do now?," "How am I going to cope now that he is gone?," and "Who will take care of me?" Also, the activities that are part of the funeral, the meetings with other mourning relatives, and other things that are happening in the days surrounding the moment of death add to the confusion, creating more unwanted anxiety as time goes on. It is understandable that the griever wonders about the loss of control over his or her emotions, the feeling of going insane, and the fear of engaging in aggressive thoughts or deeds, and the obvious inability to cope with even the smallest tasks.

For some time it was thought that *jealousy* was only associated with grief arising from separation and divorce; resulting from the individual imagining the former spouse with another.

Jealousy, however, also is a common emotional experience after death—the widow envying other women who still have their husbands; the parents who have lost a child envying, even hating other parents who still have all their children; the child feeling hateful and resentful toward other children who have parents to go home to. Even though these feelings are regarded as unnatural and unacceptable, they are often very intense and help form the basis for a feeling of guilt.

Another element to consider is *shame*. As an emotional component it can take the form of the griever being ashamed to allow others to see his true feelings, even though they are perfectly natural. But suppressing them makes the bereavement process much harder to work through. Also, because of the shame they feel, many people isolate themselves from their family and friends, and then resent them for not trying to break through their isolation. The feeling of shame may also be created by the griever being ashamed of the position in which he or she had been placed through no personal fault. Some widows openly admit that they are somewhat ashamed of their social status, and that because of that they have broken off all contact with former friends who are married.

Of all the emotional components the bereaved must deal with, *aggression* is one of the most difficult to accept and to work through, probably because of the way society views aggressive thoughts and deeds, especially when they are directed toward the dead.

In every death, there is an irritability directed against family and friends, but sometimes these feelings are totally out of proportion and turn into angry and bitter feelings, which then appear to be the overwhelming response to the loss. In a case like that, true sadness is absent, and the mourning turns into a bitter tirade against those seen as responsible for the loss. Usually this attitude is totally unjustified. While the anger and aggression may initially have been directed toward the dead for "deserting" those who are left behind, it slowly changes direction and is instead aimed at those individuals who were present at the moment of death yet did not prevent it from happening. Medical personnel—doctors and nurses—are often singled out as prime targets for this primitive rage. These responses often appear if the pre-existing relationship was one of extreme symbiotic dependence.

Also in many cases there is a *protest* against God or Fate. The anguished cries of, "God, why me?" and "I didn't deserve this. Why did You let this happen?" are most difficult to handle. But also the anguished cries directed against the person who has died can be very difficult to defuse. Whereas the grief is evidenced by obvious outbursts of crying, anger is often not all that obvious and can easily be overlooked. It is not always necessary for the anger to be expressed in an outburst in order to be processed. Sometimes it takes only an imagined conversation with the deceased to reveal the anger and aggression that has been building up, waiting to be released.

Denial plays an important part throughout the entire bereavement. The searching and the illusions are a manner of denial. With the emotional components, the denial ebbs and returns, breaks down, and comes back again in full force. In some ways it is a defensive mechanism and a protective barrier that shields the griever from receiving too much pain all at once.

The next step, that of *letting go*, is undoubtedly the most difficult for all grievers, and this is the phase that has been the goal of the therapy all along. Relinquishing the dead person, object or role is difficult, because it means a final good-bye. This step has to be taken consciously before the final steps of the therapy can be taken.

Working through bereavement is different for every individual, but no matter how it is done—whether with the help of a therapist or privately—it will eventually lead to resolution and acceptance. For some people, this awareness comes suddenly; for others, it is the result of a gradual process of awakening.

Letting go takes place when the searching diminishes and

as the emotional components are gradually extinguished so that the feelings become less intense. Then reality begins to take over. It is the moment of the *resolution* of the sorrow and grief and an *acceptance* of the new reality. In many ways it is a "leave-taking" from the dead—a peaceful acquiescence. It is the realization that life must go on, but this time in a changed form in which the departed no longer occupies the central and most dominant position in one's life.

Reintegration occurs next. This is not the easiest of the phases. It is not sufficient to realize that the dead will never return. The new awareness of the changed reality must be put into everyday practice, carrying out the consequences of the psychic changes. It is a process interrupted by many setbacks, especially on memorable occasions such as birthdays and anniversaries. Reintegration can take a long, long time and can be extremely painful. Many old habits that were once meaningful within the relationship with the departed have lost all meaning, yet they tend to persist. They have almost become ceremonial habits, and it may take years to realize that the enactment of these habits is nothing but the outward expression of a fading memory. Since the death may come at the end of a long married life or an intimate partnership of another type, these ceremonial habits may exist in many different areas. For example, going to the supermarket for a weekly shopping and buying some exotic foods. Why? Because she loved it! Stopping by at the nearest travel agency, picking up some folders about a new ski resort. Why? Because skiing was her favorite sport. Putting on that brocade dress. Why? It was his favorite. Can you see how habits like these can take a long time dying? They have become such integral parts of life that they will fade slowly, very slowly. The griever may not realize the importance of these little rituals until the realization hits that these habits began as shared experiences. At that moment a sharp pain will pierce the psyche. Suddenly she *knows* that things are somehow different now . . . and the resulting pain is devastating.

As early as 1944 it was observed that one of the big obstacles to "grief work" was the fact that so many patients try to avoid the intense distress connected with the grief experience and even shy away from giving expression to the emotions that are an essential part of grief.[7]

Dr. John Bowlby, a leading researcher in the field of personality development, former president of the International Association for Child Psychiatry, and one of the pioneers in the area of the dynamics of mourning, has taken a hard look at the reasons why the mourning of some individuals follows a pathological course, whereas that of others does not. His conclusions, which are based on more than twenty years of research, indicate that there are a number of variables that strongly influence the bereavement process. He classifies them under five specific headings:

- The identity and the role of the lost person
- The age and the sex of the bereaved
- The causes and the circumstances of the loss
- The social and psychological circumstances affecting the bereaved about the time of and after the loss
- The personality of the bereaved, with special reference to his capacities for making love relationships and for responding to stressful situations.[8]

In "the identity and the role of the lost person" we find that disordered bereavement among adolescents or children usually occurs when the lost person was a parent, or parent substitute. In other words, troubled bereavement is more likely to follow the loss of someone with whom there has been a deep-felt emotional attachment, than of someone with whom that special relationship did not exist. Children who feel extremely close to their parents, lovers whose lives are closely intertwined, spouses who have built their entire existence around a possessive love relationship are all prime candidates for a difficult and prolonged bereavement process. Yet among all these losses, the loss of a grown child may well be the "most distressing and long-lasting of all griefs." [9]

The second point, "the age and the sex of the bereaved," is also still very debatable. There is really no age at which a person is safe from a troubled bereavement. Studies conducted on psychiatric patients have clearly shown that there were a number of illnesses that were directly related to a bereavement that was encountered during the later years of life. In fact, of 121 London patients—both male and female—who were used for this survey and whose condition had developed within a short time after bereavement, twenty-one were in the age bracket of sixty-five and over.[10] Evidence to relate sex to the incidence of pathological bereavement is hard to find, even though there is no doubt that, based on pure statistics, more women than men encounter the pangs of pathological bereavement. But since the loss of a spouse does not as frequently occur to men as it does to women, it would not be fair to base our judgment on these figures.

Also, we don't know whether both sexes experience their bereavement in the same way, and what may seem borderline pathological for one may be perfectly appropriate for another one.

Bowlby's approach to "the causes and the circumstances of the loss" brings up some interesting points that give a deeper insight into the background of this problem. A protracted period of nursing prior to the death may not have as severe an effect on the survivors as a sudden and untimely death, but it may lead to other problems, such as feelings of guilt and inadequacy, and other psychological complications. Closely related to this are the state the body was in when it was last seen, how the news of the death reached the survivor, and the circumstances under which the person died. There is little doubt that a death that caused severe mutilation or one that was caused by suicide will cause stronger reactions than one that was the result of a prolonged illness.

The various beliefs and practices found among peoples belonging to various cultures or religions also have a decided influence on the bereavement process. Someone who holds that death is final, without hope for a continuation of life in the "hereafter," is apt to suffer more from the separation than someone who is firmly convinced that death is merely a temporary state that will end at the moment the survivor dies, at which time they will be reunited again. Also, the hindrance extended by family members or friends influences the course of the mourning, especially if the bereaved has been forced by economic circumstances to "move in" with the family.

Is there one specific type of personality that is prone to pathological bereavement?

No one is sure, but we do know that it is as much the individual's pattern of interaction with the deceased as the structure of the individual's personality that is responsible for the way he reacts to a loss.[11] Certainly most people suffering severe bereavement problems are those who live lives of close interaction with those around them. Some of these are highly possessive in their love or friendship ties and form strong bonds or attachments.

BEREAVEMENT OF CHILDREN

The desire for solitude and the pain and distress of the loss often lead the surviving adult or adults into conscious or subconscious attempts to exclude the children from the sadness that has invaded the family. All attention is focused on the problems surrounding the death, and the younger members of the family are usually left wandering around as if the sudden change in life affected everyone but them. But grief is a normal, however painful, reaction to the tearing of a close and loving bond that affects all of us. It is an emotional syndrome that causes anguish and takes the mourners to the summit of helplessness and hopelessness, there to be consumed by remorse, regret, anxiety and a searing feeling of hurt and utter aloneness. Yet if *we*, adults, can feel that way and experience these excruciating moments of pain, then how about the children who also see and feel the agony of death, yet don't understand?

We may not totally understand a child's view of death, but we nevertheless owe it to him to make a serious attempt to look at death through his inexperienced eyes. If there is a measure of misconception in the child's understanding of death, it is probably due to the incorrect or incomplete information we have supplied. A child can conceive and reflect the basic concepts of life correctly only if we prepare him for its treacherous ways. We cannot hide the facts of death, and there are few things more frightening to a child than to see a number of adults emotionally upset and not know the reasons why. The solitude of the funeral parlor, the hushed voices conversing in a monotonous way, the pungent odor of lilacs, the mournful, tear-stained faces of the viewers and the fear of what may be lurking behind all those closed doors all add to the mystery of death. He wants to know why he's there, why "it" happened and what it all really means, but unless we have prepared the child beforehand, the experience will be put away in his depository of fear on top of all the other things he doesn't understand but fears nevertheless.

Among all the explanations given to children, the ones telling them that the deceased has "gone to heaven," is "making a long trip," or "has gone to sleep" are those used most frequently. And they are often easy to give because usually children are not present when a relative dies, and the news of the death often reaches them after considerable delay. In fact, many of them don't find out the real truth until several years later,[12] while one study even indicated that relatively few children attend the funeral of a loved one; in fact, this specific British study mentioned eleven out of ninety-four.[13]

Most children's concept of death is very simple. When still young, schoolmates are usually the first ones to tell them about sex and death, and quite often in that order. The dead bird on the road, the dead dog, the dead fish on the riverbank all tell a child that life doesn't go on forever; that somewhere there is an element of change as yet left unexplained. A child may wonder for a while, but eventually curiosity prevails and the child begins to ask questions. "Why does a bird die? Who decides when it happens? Will he always be dead?" The answers are in large share determined by the culture and the religion of the child's parents, and because of the vast range of ideas about death, the answers may also vary greatly. To some, the death of an animal or of a human is but a stopover in the process of reincarnation; to others it means entry into an existence of eternal bliss. Still other children are told that the deceased merely rests until a resurrection, and to others death is the end of all things. Some answers give hope, but to a child it may all be very confusing.

It is easy to disregard the importance of a child's mourning, for because of his or her youth and inexperience, a child views death and its consequences differently than adults do. An adult can cope with it; a child can't as readily. An adult can ferret out information about the circumstances of the loss, but a child's queries often go unheeded. "They" can find ways to justify the loss, but for a child it seems as if the world has come to an end. Children do mourn, but exactly how they do it is still the subject of considerable discussion. In theory, childhood bereavement can be divided into six stages *or* components, meaning that they do not have to follow each other in a certain sequence but can occur simultaneously.

During the first stage their thoughts and behavior are still directed toward the lost object or person and will remain that way for a considerable length of time. Second, the hostility of the bereaved child is generally directed toward anyone in the environment and not necessarily toward the lost person. Third, there are the general appeals—even demands—for help, combined or followed by the emotions of despair, withdrawal and regression, followed by the fifth phase, which consists of reorganization of behavior directed toward a new object. The child actually undergoes his or her own bereavement process, and the only way he or she can restructure the broken relationship is by having all the answers dealing with the bereavement available. This is why children should never be shielded from the facts of death. They need and deserve a straightforward answer.

A number of years ago, a man came in for bereavement problems that appeared to have been rooted at an early age. He was about three or four years old when his mother died and, in order to spare him the agony of witnessing the funeral and seeing his mother's coffin lowered into the ground, the relatives decided to leave him home while they went to the church for the service and the subsequent burial. The sad faces, the mournful attitudes of his family members, and the inexplicable weeping had convinced him that something terrible had happened. He couldn't find his mother anywhere and no one supplied any answers. When his relatives finally left for the services, they locked him up in the house.

Within minutes after they had left, he scrambled out of a window and made his way to the church to see for himself what this sad excitement was all about. But before he could even get close to the casket, an alert relative noticed him and rushed him back to the house.

Years later during the therapy sessions, his suppressed grief surfaced—grief for the death of his mother, combined with aggression directed toward those who had tried to protect him by not allowing him to take part in the funeral service, which to him was an integral part of his bereavement problem.

In the therapy, he used his imagination to retrace his steps of years ago. Once more he climbed out of the window, hurried to the church, attended the funeral, watched the casket containing his mother being carried out of the chapel and stood silently while it was entrusted to the grave.

Children do mourn, but in their own way and in their own time. Because their values are different, their mourning may not always be for the same reasons as the mourning of adults.

An interview with a new patient a few years ago gave the impression that he might suffer from an unresolved bereavement problem. The interview revealed that his father had died when he was about six years old, and he could not remember much of what had happened for the next few years following the loss. His memory had totally blanked out. Six sessions were needed to discover that his father's death had nothing to do with the patient's bereavement problem after all. His father, a dairy farmer, was up early every morning and late to bed every night, spending all of his available time tending his cows and taking care of the farm chores. Even on the weekends his time was solely devoted to the farm, and whenever he did have time off, he was so exhausted that even then the children were not able to see him. Consequently, they hardly knew him at all. When he died, an uncle told them what had happened, and the patient vaguely recalls thinking at that time, "Oh, that's nice for him. Now he can finally have some rest and doesn't have to get up again to take care of the cows!" His lack of memory about the time surrounding his father's death was due to the fact that he did not regard the death as a significant happening, and inasmuch as nothing else of importance happened around that period in his life, the years simply faded into nothingness. There was nothing to hang his memory on, and therefore there was no lingering mourning process even though he had lost his father. This constitutes a case wherein a problem tentatively diagnosed as childhood mourning is not, in fact, mourning at all, but rather an unrelated psychological disorder.

While the mourning process of a child is still a mystery, we do know that children quite often postpone working on their mourning process until their parents have processed theirs.

Many people have noticed that once their bereavement is resolved, their children begin to work on their own bereavement process. For example, one woman's husband had been killed in an explosion. In her desire to hide her bereavement from her children, she took them on a vacation to Spain, where she and her husband had planned to visit months before. In fact, they left the day after the funeral!

For two years thereafter she tried to carry on as if nothing had happened for the sake of the children, but ultimately she became extremely depressed and had to be admitted for therapy in a mental hospital. The therapy lasted only two months, and when she returned home and the children realized that her depression was gone or, at least, had been brought under control, they began their own mourning. For the first time they asked questions about their father and soon were engrossed in burial games. Tirelessly, they and their friends would scout the neighborhood for dead birds and animals so they could hold funeral services for them. The "game" lasted several weeks, during which time even the mother brought them a dead bird.

"The pain of going through burials all over again almost killed me," she confessed, "but the children seemed to need it."

When eventually all their questions concerning their father had been answered, their preoccupation with burials ceased. They had worked through their grief, had symbolically buried their father, and their bereavement had become a thing of the past.

Their grief had finally been resolved.

A child's mourning may be expressed differently than an adult's. Yet for both, it is the past relationship with the deceased as well as the survivor's own personality that is responsible for the way he or she reacts.

A survey undertaken in 1954 as part of the Minnesota Multiphasic Personality Inventory has been used as basis for several additional studies. In one program, all the ninth-grade students attending the Minnesota schools in 1954 were singled out and divided into three groups: those from families that were still together; those from families broken because of the death of a parent; and those from families broken as the result of a divorce or separation. When these people were surveyed eighteen years later, it appeared that the different familial situations had had a decisive influence on their social and emotional development.

Of those children whose families were intact at their fifteenth year, only 8.8 percent reported having experienced a major illness eighteen years later. Those whose families had been bereaved that year reported that 17.1 percent suffered major illnesses, while those individuals who witnessed a divorce or separation in their family at that time admitted to 19.6 percent occurrence of a major illness. Of the children who had experienced an extreme emotional distress, those from whole families reported 19.9 percent; the bereaved group admitted to 33.5 percent, and the divorced or separated group led with 34.8 percent.[14] This problem has not yet received sufficient attention.

As mentioned earlier, interrupted bereavement can also result in the development of phobic reactions. These reactions are characterized by strong feelings of anxiety caused by a situation or an object that is normally harmless and presents no actual danger to the person. Any person who avoids confrontations and purposely evades problematic situations is a potential phobic. Phobias often have been thought of as attempts to cope with specific internal or external dangers by carefully avoiding situations likely to bring about whatever is feared. Grieving is one of these situations, yet this does not mean that the application of the principles of grief therapy may be the most effective treatment for all phobias. Zoophobia (the fear of animals or of some particular animal), monophobia (the fear of being alone), and other phobias can have grief as well as other causes as basis.

Let's take a look at a hypothetical example—a connection between grief and zoophobia, the term for a fear of animals.

A forty-five-year-old woman feels she is unable to manage after the recent death of her husband. In our culture, she should grieve for perhaps a year—but no longer. Yet after that year, this woman is still consumed with intense sorrow, unable really to unwind and talk about it for fear that people will think she's "odd." After all, she has been a widow for a year already and should be over the loss. Life becomes difficult for her. She becomes depressed, experiencing a high level of tension, which increases when she leaves the house.

Tearful, depressed and tense, she meanders along the sidewalk, sees a small dog and picks him up. Frightened, not knowing her intentions, the little stray attempts to bite her, and while she drops the dog, her increased attention becomes associated with the animal's hostile behavior. Looking around her, she suddenly realizes that there are many dogs on the street and that all of them are potentially dangerous to a lone woman. As a result, she becomes more and more afraid to leave her home. This, of course, increases her tension to the point where she becomes incapacitated because of her anxiety to avoid dogs. Result? Zoophobia.

Let's take a look at an actual case.

Theresa, a thirty-eight-year-old woman, was referred to us by her family doctor with the complaint that she had developed a phobia for cancer, which had put her in such a deep state of depression that she had become suicidal.

In the letter from her family doctor that she brought with her, he explained that she had been treated for cancer of the vocal cords and had been pronounced totally free of cancer approximately six months ago. Shortly thereafter, however, she had developed a cancer phobia that was so extreme that it dealt with anything even vaguely connected with the disease. It had made her suicidal, yet her cancer was 100 percent in remission, which she knew. Whereas her phobia had been merely bothersome in the beginning, it began to affect her family life. Her constant crying and irrational fear disrupted the relationship between her and her husband, and her phobia for contracting the disease again controlled her entire thinking.

This was a clear-cut phobia for a specific situation.

During the initial interview she admitted that the very idea of having cancer had been a terrible blow to her. The X-ray treatment she had undergone had left her extremely uncomfortable, and the fear of the outcome of her monthly checkups kept her in a constant state of agitation.

About the time her cancer had been discovered, her son had graduated from a merchant marine institute and anticipated

traveling for six months at a time without being able to communicate with his parents. This was very difficult for her. She
had always enjoyed a good relationship with him and this sudden emptiness in her life was more than she could endure. Her
son was only eighteen, yet he would be gone. And she didn't
expect much sympathy from her sixteen-year-old daughter, for
she too was trying to break loose from her parents and establish
herself in her own way.

Life had suddenly become too much.

Theresa's story suggested several explanations. For instance,
the departure of her son and the fact that he could not be
contacted for a six-month period would really mean that she
had lost him. This loss precipitated her phobia, but she had
chosen cancer as the most likely thing to become phobic about.

A second explanation is that the phobia had developed
because of the very unpleasant treatment she had undergone
from doctors she termed "unsympathetic." Since she could not
express her anger at them because she still needed them for
her regular checkups, she had developed a cancer phobia in
order to receive added attention. This was complicated further
by the friendship she had developed with a fellow patient in
the hospital who also had had cancer of the vocal cords.
Whereas Theresa's cancer had been local and could be cured,
her friend's cancer had spread. For six months after her own
hospitalization, Theresa had visited the woman regularly, but
every visit was so upsetting that Theresa's husband finally suggested that no more contacts be made. A few months later the
woman died, and this additional loss, coupled with guilt feelings that she had left the woman in the lurch, and the idea that
she could have been this woman, compounded Theresa's emotional instability into a cancer phobia.

Once we started our therapy sessions, all the hidden feelings
began to surface. Within the first twelve minutes of the initial
session, she broke down and cried about her son who had left
home, the loss of her son, and what he really meant to her. She
admitted she hadn't realized how much she missed him. At the

end she was encouraged to talk this over with her husband and tell him how much she missed her boy.

During the second session, Theresa explained that talking to her husband had been good for both of them because they now realized how wonderful it was for their son to achieve his life's ambition and roam the high seas. She still considered his absence a loss, but now it had been turned into a loss about which both of them could grieve together.

Was she angry at her son for leaving her? She smiled and replied, "Oh no, not at all. He always wanted to go to sea, and parents should never interfere with a child's choice!"

It was not until the third session, while she looked at his photographs, that she suddenly burst out in a fit of temper and threw the photographs about the room, exclaiming that she felt miserable about his leaving, but that he was having a good time nevertheless. She exploded into a tremendous outburst of anger about her son. It didn't last long, but the anger was there.

When she came back for the fourth time, she freely admitted that she had experienced more fits of anger since she had left the office, but that the anger was slowly subsiding. Also, for the first time, she was able to talk to her husband and friends about her son's leaving without any hard feelings. "I am sorry he is not with us," she remarked, "but I accept it now and understand that he has to go his own way."

The connection between the "loss" of her son and her cancer phobia had clearly been established, but it was not finished as yet. It took a total of thirteen sessions to clear up her anger at the doctors, to erase her guilt feelings about having left the patient who eventually died, and to accept the fact that her cancer phobia would not bring her son back.

At the end of the therapy Theresa's depression had disappeared and the phobia had vanished.

There is a strong relationship between phobias and grief. Indeed, phobic reactions can be triggered by a bereavement or other form of loss, and no one is immune to its snares. In fact, anyone who feels emotionally threatened and who usually avoids confrontations or difficult situations may unknowingly become a phobic through his or her avoidance behavior. This, in turn, can lead to an emotional disturbance.

In Guided Confrontation Therapy this link between bereavement and phobic behavior is recognized and addressed. In fact, GCT was developed at the University of Amsterdam's Phobia Project as the result of extensive work with phobic patients where flooding with prolonged exposure showed its positive aspects.

Even though great advances have been made in understanding the human mind, it is still difficult to isolate the reason why one person's grief follows a normal pathway to extinction and another's doesn't. In cases of unresolved bereavement, however, the techniques employed in Guided Confrontation Therapy show much promise, for they aim at the extinction, not the suppression, of negative emotions.

Thus, through the aid of GCT, people beset by grief and the emotional disturbances unresolved bereavement can create have another chance at life—a *new* life, far removed from the agony of the past and the sad memories of grief.

CHAPTER FOUR

Is Divorce the Right Cure for a Sick Marriage?

DIVORCE HAS ONCE BEEN described as the most belittling experience an adult can undergo. It is the place in marriage where the illusion of beauty fades and the harshness of reality takes over. To hundreds of thousands this definition is a true reflection of a marriage gone sour.

In Western culture, the divorce rate is skyrocketing. It is as if the marriage-breakup syndrome has found a "black hole" without end, an Orion without limits—ever expanding. Yet, the relief and happiness people expect from divorce frequently turn into sadness and anger, for even though both partners may agree to split up at the end of a "bad" marriage, the mixture of emotions involved usually results in a depression for at least one of them.

"I thought this divorce would really solve all my problems," one woman admitted, "but I've been crying myself to sleep for days. Perhaps he wasn't so bad after all. Do you think that maybe I really didn't hate him all that much?"

The dissolution of a deep human relationship is a harsh and painful process that affects not only the two partners but also their children and often their close relatives and friends as well. The idea advanced by psychologists and some marriage counselors that the breakup syndrome is the beginning of a new era of "freedom for liberated people" isn't at all what it's cracked up to be. Divorce is *not* the ultimate solution to cure the ills of a sick marriage.

Observes Paul Bohannan:

"One reason it feels so good to be newly married is the sensation that, out of the whole world, *you* have been selected. *One reason divorce feels so awful is that you have been deselected.*"[1]

He couldn't be more right.

We live in a family-oriented culture, and whereas falling in love carries society's blessing, falling out of love creates its own special stigma.

Dr. James L. Framo, a family therapist and professor of psychology at Temple University, believes "Divorce does not mean defeat. It may mean victory over an initially neurotic choice of mate." And he continues, "Do you know the Chinese word for crisis? It contains two characters. One means danger; the other, opportunity. Well, divorce is a true crisis. Obviously it presents danger; but properly handled, it can be what it's often called—getting your freedom. Freedom from guilt, anger, self-pity, desire for revenge . . . and freedom to love again."[2]

But in many cases it is a freedom with pain, and no matter how much liberty comes with the divorce decree, it is still a major emotional crisis that has its own special hurts and won't go away unless something positive is done about it. To look upon a divorce merely as a part of a general growth process with healthy positive angles is plainly a cop-out. That a marriage breakup may be a necessity in certain cases is something we can't argue about, but just because you are allowed to exercise the right to disentangle does not mean that the result will be instant happiness and freedom from stress.

S. Gettleman and J. Markowitz in their book *The Courage to Divorce*[3] also imply that divorce has only positive aspects. They regard divorce as an important means to find one's own identity. Loneliness and sorrow as emotions have, according to them, no place within this process of separation. Reality, however, disagrees sharply with this point of view. Divorce is a painful affair that can have all the overtones of intense bereavement. Holmes and Rahe give a divorce a stress rating of 73 units on their Social Readjustment Rating Scale, placing it just after the death of a spouse. But this rating is on the conservative side. The struggle for freedom takes its toll.

By the time the divorce finally takes place, it is at the conclusion of a long history of arguments, serious disagreements, physical fights and numerous attempts to patch up a ragged relationship. These emotional upsets seesaw back and forth until the negative aspects of the marriage outweigh the positive, and one of the partners finally exclaims, "I've had it! I want OUT!" Even at this point it is not over, for now the disagreements move from the emotional to the legal stage. One of the partners must find another place to live, which in itself is very disruptive for both of them. For the one who stays behind, there is the pain of dividing the possessions and watching some of the familiar and treasured objects carried out the door. The very act of *actually seeing things go* still creates an emptiness in the life of both partners, increasing, instead of diminishing, the already existing stress.

Psychologists now use the term "bereavement" to describe the pains of divorce, as well as loss from the death of a loved one. While in a case of death, loss is absolute and unchangeable, in both cases it is a serious breakdown in an emotionally charged relationship.

Most people find it more difficult to get through a divorce-bereavement than to resolve one that has been caused by death —this in direct contradiction to the rating found on the Social Readjustment Rating Scale.

As a recent divorcee remarked:

"If my ex-husband were only dead, it would make everything so much easier. I'd get over my problems so much faster."

Can this be because the mourning process after a death follows a path that appears preordained, and the feeling of loss and the emotional upheavals following a divorce are emotions for which there are no prescribed ritualistic behaviors?

Compared to bereavement from death, the process following a divorce is highly complex. If the relationship before the divorce was of the love-hate variety, then a resulting bereavement will be extremely difficult to resolve.

At the beginning of the breakup, one or both partners experience mounting feelings of anger. This turns into despair, depression and finally aggression. In bereavement due to death, aggression seldom appears immediately. Also with a divorce, the ex-partner is still alive, and by living is a daily reminder of rejection. His or her very existence is a threat to the grieving spouse, for even though the two have legally agreed to sever the marriage ties, *a relationship still exists,* even though in a changed form. With death one must eventually face the reality that the partner is gone forever, but with a divorce there is still a lingering uncertainty, a feeling that perhaps it is not really permanent; that he or she may still come back—someday! What makes it even more difficult is the sexual contacts that are often kept alive even though the divorce has become an established fact. Twelve percent of all divorced partners continue their sexual contact with each other during the first two months after the divorce, and more than half of the divorcees admit that the ex-partner was the first one they called in cases of emergency. This, combined with care of the children, visitation rights, alimony and child support, keeps the relationship alive. Chances of seeing the ex-partner again at the home of friends they once shared also complicates things. These perchance (or sometimes planned) meetings are enough to ignite that little spark of hope into a brightly burning ember, only to have it carelessly extinguished later on. In a divorce, it is rare to find both partners equally vehement in their desire to separate and equally hateful of one another. These lingering feelings of hope make the total acceptance of a divorce extremely difficult.

Ending the bereavement is also hindered by the lack of acceptance of the new situation by friends and relatives. "Friends" withdraw, either because in their own marriage relationship the reality of divorce cannot be faced, or possibly because their social life can only accommodate a "couple" and not a "single." So the divorce does not merely mean a leave-taking from the ex-partner, but from a number of friends as well, who will begin to split their allegiance. Those who remain are confused as to whether to console or to congratulate the divorcee.

In-laws, too, present a problem, especially if the relationship has been a good one. But the greatest loser in a divorce process may not be the warring partners but the child who has become an unwilling pawn in the conflict. During the years before the divorce, the child may have been used—wittingly or unwittingly —by both parents against each other. When the differences between the parents finally erupt into open hostility, resulting in the instigation of divorce proceedings, the child will also have reached his or her peak of emotional distress and will experience terrible anguish trying to determine on whose side his or her loyalty should be. The crushing emotional blow, however, does not occur until the divorce actually takes place. Even though this final parting dispels the stressful atmosphere in the home, the actual breakup between the parents is something children usually don't and can't understand. Suddenly one of the parents has moved out for good, and this becomes the starting point for a barrage of questions. "Why did he leave *me?*" "Doesn't he love *me* either?" "Will he ever come back and kiss me good night again?" The agony that pulsates through a child's mind at the moment of divorce and often for years after may completely alter the child's values and affect his or her attitude toward future relationships. The child feels deserted, lost, unloved and becomes afraid to "give" or trust. Eventually the child can become locked in a private bereavement process, with his or her limited vocabulary preventing a full airing of fears.

But this is only the beginning.

Having been assigned to one of the parents by the court, the child now becomes a constant witness to the smoldering tension between the parents whenever the other one claims him or her for the weekly or monthly visitation rights. *Again* the child is confronted with making choices as to loyalty, even though the parents have already finalized their choice, and for years and years this will continue. The parent who has custody may have resolved his or her grief, but for the child there is no such luxury. The pressure of a changed lifestyle combined with the divided loyalty problems can produce a "moderate life crisis."

A divorce involving children is never a final separation, and the distress felt by one of the partners is apt to be stronger and more lasting if the children serve as points of continuing contact.

Some people think that it is only the analogy between death and divorce that frightens people. Yet nothing is farther from the truth. In divorce we are dealing with various gradations of grief and stages of the bereavement process. It is impossible to compare bereaved individuals and come to a conclusion that one suffers more than another. Everyone experiences the bereavement process in his own way, and various facets of his personality determine how he works it through. Usually if divorce therapy is indicated, it is often the last step on a path that has led from a helpful neighbor to a marriage counselor or family counselor. It is the counselor's job to attempt to reconcile the two disputing parties, and when it becomes obvious that the relationship cannot be repaired and too much damage has been done, then the counselor will try to help the partners separate with the least amount of emotional damage. Counseling changes perspective, scope and aims and becomes a process of disentangling the couple. After the separation has become an established fact, most people move through the final phases of disentanglement in their own way and in their own time, and those who have gone through the process successfully eventually become ready to live a new life.

But not everyone is that fortunate. Inasmuch as the separation from someone who was once very close involves emotional distress, it does create mourning. And this mourning *has* to be experienced, and it *has* to be worked through. If not, one is setting oneself up for serious emotional problems.

S. Kessler in his book *The American Way of Divorce: Pre-*

scription for Change, remarks, "Mourning helps you rid your-self of the ghost. If the process does not happen following separation or divorce, chances are it will appear unexpectantly at a later point in time." [4] Mourning enables us to withdraw our-selves from reality and gives us a chance to rearrange our emotions and test out the new situation.

And in a divorce, this is often a necessity, for there may be much to mourn about.

The phases and components of divorce bereavement are very similar to those that are found in death bereavement already outlined in Chapter Three, and their sequences and intensity too may vary from case to case. *Anger* over what has happened is always present if the griever has finally come to the realiza-tion that outside help has become necessary. The emotions of divorced persons may fluctuate between feelings of intense sor-row and depression on one side and near-uncontrollable fits of raging anger on the other. It frightens them, because many never have experienced such an intense emotional upheaval directed toward their ex-partner. *Guilt* also plays a prominent role in divorce, with the idea of "not having done enough" to save the marriage playing an important role. The anger and guilt may be brought to within reasonable limits of control, but this does not mean that the *depression,* with all its melancholia and feelings of desperate loneliness, has also been resolved. Despair is more frequent among those recently divorced than among individuals of approximately the same age enjoying basi-cally the same socioeconomic status, but still married.

Despair and *desolation* are other components that everyone who goes through a divorce process has to take into account, and they cannot be avoided or ignored. *Denial* of the reality of the new situation is another component that keeps coming to the forefront. The newly separated individual simply cannot fully comprehend the loss of emotional investment she or he has made over a span of, let's say, ten or fifteen years. No matter the problems encountered, there *were* some good moments too, and the sudden shock, the finality of the separation, often has a benumbing effect. In fact, denial is one of these roaming phases that seems to interject itself throughout the entire bereavement, fading in and out of the picture with gentle persistence, ever present, always present to interrupt.

A number of years ago, a pathetic denial phase of desertion-bereavement that began with tragic overtones came to our attention. Yet it ended on such a positive note that it should be shared here. It was a case handled by a psychologist who had followed a grief-therapy workshop and reported on it at a later date.

It concerned a young child whose father had suddenly left the house and never returned. The abrupt and unexpected desertion had such a devastating effect on one of his children that it was necessary to seek the assistance of a guidance counselor. As is usual in the case of a new client, certain basic information regarding her background and problems was assembled, and the results of the psychological tests that were administered indicated that there was not much hope that something constructive could be done to alleviate the problem of inattentiveness, total apathy and unruliness. Her behavioral problems were highly complex, and inasmuch as there did not seem to be much that could be done, the psychologist attached to the guidance clinic decided to bring his newly acquired training in grief therapy into practice, recognizing that the little girl could not accept the fact that her daddy had walked out on her.

Probing the family background, he perceived the definite impression that the mother also had difficulty working through her grief, so he asked that she attend all the therapy sessions. The child was withdrawn and silent during the early sessions. Therefore, the attention was focused on the mother instead, and under gentle probing, she slowly relaxed and began to talk about the father and the changes that had taken place in the home since his hasty departure. Eventually the young child began to show interest in the therapy and started to participate, sharing her unresolved grief along with her mother's. At approximately the fourth sitting, the little girl insisted that inasmuch as her brother and sister had the same problem, they too should attend the therapy sessions. Soon the therapy, which had begun as a one-to-one relationship, blossomed into a family therapy program dealing with the life crisis caused by the father deserting the family. It was not until the sixth and final session that the dramatic climax occurred. The session had scarcely started when the therapist asked the little girl to draw the "ideal" family. Painstakingly, she began to draw a daddy, a mommy and three children sitting around a table.

"That's fine," the therapist commented, "but your daddy has left you—so what are you going to do with him?"

"Well, I guess we'll have to cut him out," the child replied, and taking a pair of scissors, she quickly eliminated him from the picture.

"And what now?" he asked. "What will you do with him now?"

She looked at him for a moment, and suddenly she knew the only answer that would satisfy her.

"Well, it's very sad," she replied thoughtfully, "but Daddy has to go into the garbage pail because he has left us." This one move led to emotional outbursts and a display of grief by the entire family. When it subsided they all realized that Daddy was no longer a part of the family. He was gone forever! It was a child's way of dealing with grief and coming to an acceptance that a certain situation had actually taken place. It was a sad story, yet in the end she displayed a bravery that was well beyond her years.

Jealousy plays more of a role in divorce grief than in grief due to death. Not only is jealousy's role more important, but also the emotion is stronger. The fact that the ex-partner is still alive and may be attempting to build a new life can elicit emotions of jealousy so powerful that they become almost an obsession. Sitting at home all alone, afraid to visit their mutual friends and wondering whether the divorce was really the best solution to their problems, a woman may let her mind wander, imagining her ex-husband going out with the woman she wished she could have been. She may keep her mind focused on the idea of her ex-husband starting a new relationship, her jealousy mounting, even though their parting was the climax of a contentious and hateful relationship.

Shame or *embarrassment* may follow the feelings of jealousy, but it is more likely that shame or embarrassment will start the instant the news of the divorce leaks out. It is one of the separation anxieties that can be found in almost every divorce. In fact, shame makes its entry the moment a divorce is being contemplated but does not become an identifiable "component" until the reality of the divorce is undeniable. This emotion is stronger and more obvious in cases of divorce than in the aftermath of death. It is not really shameful to have lost your husband or wife. There are, of course, some widows who feel ashamed of being alone, but this is separate from the feelings they have about losing their husband. After all, he did not leave voluntarily. He was *taken* against his will. But this is never the case with either open desertion or divorce. No matter how well concealed the entire divorce action may have been, the outcome is the same. It results in both partners living alone, and at least one of them desires no further contact.

Then why the feeling of shame?

It is because of their inability to make a success of the union. A divorce is the result of failure. It takes two people to make a marriage, and it takes the same two to break it up. In death, there usually is an innocent partner; in divorce, never. When two people agree to disagree, both have had their input into the marriage relationship, and both have failed to a greater or lesser degree. Yet those who can recognize this in other marriages are seldom able to see it in their own. Divorce is a broken relationship, and most people recognize the complicity of both partners in the breakup. As far as "others" are concerned, there really is no innocent party.

Indeed, there are many reasons for harboring feelings of shame, and because of the circumstances leading up to them, they are stronger in a broken marriage relationship than in a parting due to death.

Other components of divorce grief such as protest, aggression, resolution and acceptance and finally reintegration, which are all indispensable elements of the process, are more relevant to the stages of the actual therapy than to the recognition of the dominant emotions.*

The "new life" that follows the bereavement is an area of great concern to the social sciences and has been identified by different names. Some call it the "second adolescence," a "reorientation of lifestyle and identity" or a "process of self-renewing," but although the names vary, they all describe the same process.

When this stage in the recovery program has been reached, the various phases and components of the process overlap.

Remember: Divorce does not mean that you have been defeated in everything. Whether you have gone through therapy to resolve your problem or have managed to work through your bereavement on your own power, it is important that you get to a point where you reach out for the future, ready to embrace it with a renewed sense of enthusiasm for life. Also, at this point, the realization that marriage had both good and bad aspects begins to dawn, and even though this does not mean that you are willing to return to the predivorce days, it does indicate that you are accepting reality.

And this enthusiasm can lead to marriage all over again, for not only have the divorces in our Western society increased sharply, but so also have the remarriages. Statistics reveal that the remarriage figures almost doubled in the period 1972–74 as compared to the figures available for the years 1942–50. What the new 1980 United States Census will show is still unknown, but research conducted by the psychologists A. J. Norton and P. C. Glick in 1976 indicates that 80 percent of all divorced women (and widows) eventually remarry. Norton and Glick claim that the percentages for men are slightly higher. Other

* See Appendix under "Divorce Grief" for additional guidelines.

social scientists place the chances of remarriage for divorced women of twenty years of age at 97 percent; those of thirty-year-old women at 80 percent, and those of women forty years of age at 50 percent. So a divorce is not the end of the line—not by far. However, second marriages are not as stable as the first one. In fact, the divorce percentages climb with the second, the third and the fourth marriage, and the one out of fifteen divorced couples who try it all over again with the same partner have only a 50–50 chance of success.

What is the answer, and where is it?

Can it be found in a further liberalization of divorce laws, or has society become too liberal and loose in its interpretation of "till death us do part" and torn the value of "love, honor, cherish and obey" down with it? Is it possible that our Western culture has degenerated to such an extent that the family circle has lost all value?

The Dutch psychologist Marlies Terstegge has identified the reasons for the change in divorce rates in our Western society, and those she has listed under the social areas may be the most significant.

Let's take a look at them:

- *The increasing industrialization in the Western countries coincides with an increase in the divorce rate.* This holds true for most countries, with the exception of Japan. Closely related to industrialization is urbanization. Divorce increases in the heavy population centers. The increased mobility in these countries also carries its share of the responsibility, because the average city dweller comes in contact with more different people in one week today than a village dweller in her entire life in years past.

- *Legal changes.* The possibility of getting a divorce by mail, obtaining quick divorces by mutual agreement, a general liberalization of the divorce laws and a more

liberal interpretation of even those laws undoubtedlv
share in the responsibility.

- *Changes in the legal and social position of women.* The
  number of women who are both housewives and employees has increased steadily. They are no longer solely
  dependent on their marriage for economic survival. The
  threat of divorce is no longer a frightening prospect, and
  they feel they can take more risks. Women holding jobs
  that give them the needed security and self-esteem no
  longer look upon marriage as the only way to gain personal satisfaction. Financial independence is as important
  as emotional fulfillment, but financial independence still
  does take second place, for when the job market for
  women shrinks, the divorce rates decline also. Divorce
  rates have also declined during periods of economic depression.

- *Changing attitudes toward sexuality.* A greater degree of
  sexual freedom for both men and women thanks to con-
  traceptives has made both sexually independent. Extra-
  marital affairs no longer carry the social stigma they used
  to in times past, although men are still more "equal" and
  "privileged" than women in this area.

- *Marriage is only one of the acceptable ways of living together.* Other forms of cohabitation are now tolerated.
  Also, there is a new acceptance of those who desire to
  live alone, whatever the reason may be.

- *Because marriages between younger partners are on the
  increase,* the chance that they are the result of immature
  decisions is very great. Often a divorce appears the only
  way out of a hasty union.

- *The criteria for a "good marriage" have been down-
  graded,* and this factor in turn has lowered the divorce
  barrier. [5]

Is there *really* an answer?

Perhaps it is found in the words of the Dutch psychologist Rood-de Boer.

"We live in a consumer's society," she reasons. "We buy nothing that is intended for our entire life, and throw away everything that is old, used or old-fashioned. . . . We don't look for a lifetime job nor for a house for 'always.' We change constantly.

"This form of consumer life will eventually influence our attitude toward marriage and divorce." [6]

It already has.

CHAPTER FIVE

ϒϒϒϒϒϒ

Six Days to Sanity

IN MAY 1973, a tragic accident in a British campground took the lives of Beverley, a twelve-year-old high-school girl, and her favorite grandmother. A single candle flame, out of control, reduced a camping trailer to ashes and created unbelievable havoc in the lives of an unsuspecting family.

The sad event would probably have gone unnoticed were it not for the fact that Rita, the woman who spanned the bridge between these two generations, had become severely "stunted" in her bereavement. Instead of resolving her grief and accepting her loss, she soon sank into prolonged periods of intense emotional agony, endless hours of crying and a total unwillingness to accept the death of her mother and daughter. Her yearning for the deceased became uncontrollable. Losing her mother and daughter within half a year after the death of her father was more than she could handle.

There is much that conventional psychology and psychiatry can do in cases like this, yet here the available therapies had no measurable effect. She was unconsolable. Her physician, consulting psychiatrists, and even faith healers were at a total loss. Finally, the debilitating grief set a chain of events in motion that ultimately led to the University of Amsterdam's Phobia Project, resulting in a treatment with Guided Confrontation Therapy.

The therapy sessions were conducted in a London hotel. Trusting that her therapy might be of help to others in similar situations, she allowed CBS's "60 Minutes" program to film the sessions for release on the CBS Television Network.

Inasmuch as Rita flatly refused even to acknowledge Beverley's death, the entire first session was aimed at getting her to realize that the accident had really happened, and that Beverley would never come back.

Guided by leading questions, she recalled the facts of the tragedy.

"Well, my mother had bought a new caravan after my father died, and we weren't really going anywhere that weekend because the weekend before we had just come back from a holiday here in London. Beverley had been playing with a friend, and this friend had suddenly decided to go home with another friend, which upset her very much. So on the spur of the moment we were taking my mother to the caravan and I asked her if she would like Beverley to go home with her. And we came home. That was on a Saturday morning. . . .

"At half past six Sunday morning the doorbell rang, and there was a policeman and he said there had been an accident at the place where the caravan was. The nearest town to that was Edgefield. My mother was all right, but Beverley was dead. We went to the police station . . . and they told my husband there had been a fire. . . .

"Beverley never slept without a light. Mother suffered from osteoarthritis, and her fingers were distorted, and the door to the caravan was very stiff. After my father died she took sleeping pills and had taken a pill that night.

"What had happened, Beverley had gotten out of bed and told my mother, 'Nana, I am too hot.' And before anyone realized it the caravan was on fire. The people on the site came rushing to help, and managed to get the door open, but my mother was shielding Beverley. They pulled my mother out but didn't realize that Beverley was still in it and closed the door . . . and my mother's face was burned and she couldn't tell them that Beverley was still inside. . . .

After this recognition of the accident, Rita admitted that she had tried to face the harsh reality of having to live on without her daughter, but that everything she saw or did always reminded her of Beverley.

"I get upset when I see her friends on the road who are 14½ now and such pretty young ladies. It still hurts me. The other day we were going somewhere in a hurry and my husband said, 'Shut your eyes,' because he was taking me down a road near where she used to go to school, and I said, 'No, I've got to face up to it sometime,' but of course it was terribly painful. . . . I always thought that when you reach a certain pitch of pain that your heart stopped, but I am afraid that it doesn't. Your heart goes on and so does the pain. . . ."

But Guided Confrontation Therapy does not aim at avoiding the pain caused by grief; rather it uses it to extinguish the steps of the bereavement process eventually. To lead up to this process, Rita was asked to close her eyes and try to imagine Beverley as she was.

"I close my eyes. She is quite tall, slim, with long, light brown hair and beautiful blue eyes with very long eyelashes. She had lovely straight teeth and a very lively personality. She could be a twirp but she was very affectionate and friendly, and when the accident happened no one had to say 'Beverley who?' for everyone knew her. She was very popular at school, she made lots of friends and looked so lovely in her school uniform, and there were no problems at all and they were terribly shocked. The headmistress came to the funeral, and there were hundreds and hundreds of people and we had to have extra cars for the flowers. . . . She was a very popular little girl."

At this point in the first day's therapy session Rita was asked to picture Beverley as she was, telling herself that she would never see her again, that she was dead and gone forever.

When told that Beverley was really dead and that there was no chance of getting her back again, Rita responded:

> "I don't want her dead . . . lovely twelve-year-old girl . . . I'll never be able to do things with her. All our plans and hopes are ruined. We worked so hard for years and years to give her a nice home and get her everything she wanted and send her to a nice school. We were married six years before we had her and we wanted a daughter, and then we had a son. We were so pleased we had a boy and a girl. Our family was complete. We never imagined life without her."

She questioned:

> "What I want to know is what will I have left? It seems wrong to go anywhere without her. Can I start saying she is not here and she is never coming back? I'll be denying her existence!"

At this point the transcript of the session becomes very pointed and the effort at breaking through the denial heads for a direct confrontation.

Therapist: But she is not coming back. Her life stopped at the age of twelve, and you have to go on without her.
Rita: *I've been trying to do that for 2½ years, and it's very rough.*
But Beverley stopped at the age of twelve. You have to go on; you have to go on without her and you have to tell yourself that everything you are going to do from now on will be without her. Try to imagine her as she was, and tell her that you are going on without her. Try to tell her that. Tell her that you have to go on!
But I don't want to go on without her. . . .
But you have to! You do want her but you have to go on without her. . . .

She will think that I will forget about her.

You will *not* forget about her, but you will have to go on. Tell her that you will go on without her.

How can I think of her and let her go feeling that I deserted her?

I cannot help you there. . . . You have to desert her!

I know I have to let go, but she is part of me. It's like an amputation. There's nothing left except the pain. . . .

And you have to desert her. . .

It is a desertion. . . .

Yes. . . .

It is a desertion but I have to go on without her. But I still want to love her but it will be in a different way.

Can you close your eyes, and imagine standing at her grave and tell her that you're going away without her? Tell her, "Beverley, you are in your grave. You have to stay there. That is your place," and you as her mother, as a person, have to go on without her. Tell her! Tell her that there are times that you will be thinking of other people and other things; imagine yourself standing at her grave and tell her that you are going away. Tell her that you are leaving her. You've got to do it, Rita! Tell her that you've got to leave her!

This will be the first week I have ever missed going to the grave. . . .

Tell her why you are leaving her!

But I still care. . . .

But in a different way. You cannot go on like that.

I usually go with the flowers on a Friday. . . .

Today *is* Friday. . . . Imagine going to her grave and this time tell her, "Beverley, I am leaving you behind. You're dead, and you will have to stay there. I am leaving you." Tell her!

She was very happy when we had her. . . .

Once you start confronting yourself it usually turns out that it was not quite as bad as you had expected, and you have

to work with that knowledge; going further with that confrontation. You will have to take the next step and it is going
to be terrible.

For a little while the relentless pressure to forget Beverley
was eased somewhat, and made way for an emotional good-bye
to Rita's mother. Then Rita mentioned certain tunes Beverley
used to like, and the loss of Beverley came once again in full
focus. She recalled tunes like "Tie a Yellow Ribbon 'Round the
Old Oak Tree" and "When Will I see You Again?" and it
brought her close to an emotional breakdown.

But you will never see her again!

Yes. . . .

Can you try to listen to that tune that you liked so
much in your mind *now?* Just try! Please try. . . . Please
try. . . .

Oh Beverley. . . .

You have to face it again. You can't go running away from
it. You have to face it. I am sorry that I can't ease the pain.
You have to face it. Please try. . . .

*It's painful just to think of it, but face it. . . . I feel sick
when I do. But I can think of it . . . I can.*

The second therapy session started early the next morning.
Since the loss of her mother seemed slightly easier for Rita than
Beverley's death, it was decided to concentrate on saying a final
good-bye to Rita's mother.

*How can I get over the habit of wanting to telephone her
every day?*

That is something you will have to face. You will never be
able to talk to her, tell yourself that. Imagine looking at that
phone and telling yourself that. Imagine how she was in
the hospital and tell yourself that you will never be able to
telephone her again!

I never can. . . .

Try to tell her that it hurts that you will never be able to
telephone her again. . . .

It hurts me very much.

Tell her how much it hurts you. . . .

It disturbs me. . . .

The refusal to face the loss was still there, although its
strength was lessening. Yet the idea of addressing her mother
and telling her that she would never talk to her again and that
she didn't blame her for Beverley's death was difficult for her.
Finally she overcame her resistance.

Rita, tell her that you will never be able to talk to her and
never be able to talk to her on the phone again. She has
caused you tremendous pain, and now you have to say good-
bye to her!

I can't say good-bye. Is that wrong?

No, it's quite normal, but you have to make use of that to say
good-bye to her. . . . Tell her that you are never going to
phone her again! Tell her!

A few minutes later she began to say good-bye.

*I am sorry. . . . I will never forget you. We don't blame
you . . . at all. I am very sorry that you didn't achieve all
the things you wanted to do with us and the children, and
I hope you'll forgive me for not being able to tell you that
because I didn't realize how little time I had. I was lucky
in a way. Some girls lose their mothers years before but I
had you through the hurts. . . . It is so hard getting
through the days without you, particularly the mornings.
If I could just talk to you every morning . . . You used
to tell me all your troubles. Now I have nobody to tell my
troubles to. . . . But I have to let go of you and leave you
with Beverley and pick up the pieces and do what I can
with what's left. I'll be always thankful that we did what
we did when we could. . . . At least I've got that to look
back on. . . . I am glad. . . .*

Do you think you said good-bye?

Yes. . . .

I think so too. How do you know you've said good-bye?

*I feel different. It's hard to describe . . . as though she
was there and now she isn't. I think that in the future when
I think of her I will think of her slightly different. Slightly
to the side with room for something else in front. I hope
that's a step forward.*

It is. A big step. I am very glad for you that you could do it.
Let's stop for today.

*When I woke up this morning I knew what was going to
happen today and I felt like getting sick. . . .*

In Dutch we say, "You came here with lead in your shoes."
You're leaving here today a lot lighter. There's a lot of lead
that has been shed.

*Yes, I feel lighter. . . . I can't describe it, but I do feel dif-
ferent. I can't put it into words. The sun is shining outside
. . . perhaps I can go for a walk outside.*

The third session was not as productive as those on the first
two days. The emotional upset caused by the first two sessions
had taken its toll and Rita was emotionally, physically and mentally exhausted. Yet since she had been the one to suggest that
Beverley went to stay with her mother, it was decided to explore some of the guilt feelings and some of the aggression she
might be feeling. Early in the third session she mentioned that
for some unknown reason her husband had taken the fire extinguisher from her mother's trailer, and that if it had been
there, things might have turned out differently.

Could it be that there was not only guilt, but also a feeling
of aggression toward her husband? The suggestion was made
that she express her resentment about this vocally.

*I don't . . . I couldn't honestly say that I could be angry
with him.*

Can you close your eyes and imagine telling him that it
was just bloody stupid of him to take the fire extinguisher

away, that he should not have done that sort of thing?

No, he knows he shouldn't have done it. I couldn't.

Rita, if you say "I couldn't," that indicates to me that there
is something there. If you could do it quite easily then I'd
say, "OK, there's no need to."

*Oh, I couldn't do that. . . . It would destroy him if I sug-
gested that. . . .*

I am not suggesting that you say it to him, to his face. I am
asking you that you say it now in your imagination. To
imagine a scene with him; to tell him that it was damned
stupid to take that fire extinguisher!

Yes, it was stupid. I don't know why he did it.

Yes, it was just damned stupid; it was a present given to your
mother. Tell him that!

He shouldn't have taken it. It was only a small one.

He shouldn't have taken it.

*He shouldn't. But he admits that even if he had not taken
it, with my mother's fingers she wouldn't have used it any-
way—but still it might have helped.*

Can you in your imagination tell him what a bloody
stupid, idiotic thing it was to do to take that fire extinguisher?

*Yes, it was a stupid thing to do. He shouldn't have taken
it. We found out later that the fire-fighting facility on the
caravan site was exceedingly poor, and they told my brother
that if it was any consolation, the same thing would not
happen again. But it was too late for us.*

Hardly a consolation. Can you once again in your own imagination tell your husband what a stupid thing it was to do?
Repeat it!

It was a stupid thing to do.

Go through the scene in your mind. Tell him!

He should not have taken it.

Tell *him*, not me in your imagination.

*It was wrong. He shouldn't have taken it . . . he shouldn't
have taken it at all. It should have been put in the*

caravan and left there. It was a stupid thing to do
. . . and as it turned out it was a wicked thing to do.
We don't know these things, do we. We all make mistakes
and then we have to pay for them. The funny thing is she
really wouldn't have needed a light because it didn't grow
dark until late. But I think my mother felt probably that
when she woke late in the night she might be afraid.

Don't you feel guilty about not having trained them to sleep
without lights?

No, no. . . .

I have to explore this sort of thing to find out. And this light
in the caravan was put in an egg cup, wasn't it?

Yes. My mother didn't realize it was an egg cup. A plastic
egg cup. I haven't seen it. I don't know what it was like.
She should really have put the night-light on the saucer or
something like that, but she didn't realize that. We can
only assume what happened was that the flame caught the
edge of the cup it was in. They never established the cause
of the fire, and I was so ill at the time, I really didn't want
to know, and still don't. As far as I know the caravan almost
burned out completely. . . .

Her mind was beginning to drift back to the accident itself,
shying away from the circumstances that had connected her
husband to the fire. If there were any guilt feelings or anger
toward her husband at all, they would have to be brought to
the surface in order to be extinguished. So once again she was
asked to face them.

Can you once again tell your husband what a damned stupid
thing it was to do?

It was a stupid thing to do. . . .

You don't have to tell him but you can do it here. Do you feel
any anger when you think about it?

No, only that it was such a senseless thing to do. It was
senseless of him to take it.

But surely it is reasonable to feel anger even if something is senseless. . . .

But he doesn't often do stupid things!

OK, often or not, he did *that*, and it was a stupid thing to do.

Yes, and another thing we did. My mother had proper night-lights until that day, with a tiny battery in a bowl, and moving the things from the old caravan into the new, we had to bring a lot of things home from the old caravan, and I brought the night-light and Ian [her son] messed with it and broke it, and I didn't want to tell Mother that he'd broken it. So had she had that little light there would not have been a naked light at all. So that was another thing on my conscience. . . .

They had proper night-lights and you took them home!

Yes, it got broken at home.

So it was your fault as well.

Yes, yes, it was my fault . . . how stupid.

Yes, there you are sitting now in pain and misery and it's your own damned fault!

Yes, it is my own fault, so now you know why I feel guilty.

So what do you do about it? ·

It's too late to do anything. The damage has been done.

And you know it's your fault. . . .

Yes, it's my fault.

OK, how do you punish yourself?

Only by going over and over again saying, "I wish, I wish . . ."

You know you did it, and it's your fault. . . .

I wish I hadn't done it, but I did it.

You can't change it. Beverley is dead; your mother is dead all because of a stupidity on your part.

Yes.

You didn't have the guts to tell your mother that the light had been broken.

I didn't know the caravan was going to go on fire. I didn't even know that she was going to use a night-light. How many times do people do stupid things that don't have disastrous consequences? Why should the things I do have such disastrous consequences?

Are you trying to tell me that it wasn't your fault?

Oh no, it was my fault.

OK, it's your fault. You were stupid.

Yes.

Go ahead and tell yourself how stupid you are.

How stupid! We haven't gotten anything dangerous at home. Never occurred to me that there would be any danger. We're always so careful. We tried to protect her in every way we could, and then we go and do a stupid thing like that . . . stupid . . . senseless!

Your fault . . .

I can see myself now saying to my mother, "We were arranging to call for her. We would like Beverley to go with you—just on the spur of the moment." Just like that. I don't think I ever asked my husband.

You sent her off, and you know that there weren't any safe night-lights; you knew she needed a light every night. . . .

I really thought she would be going to bed while it was light. I never thought about the light or anything like that.

So what you are telling me now is that it might have been stupid not to have the night-light there, but you did not think about it.

Had I slept in the caravan I would have realized about the lighting. But we had never slept there. . . .

So how can you say it was your fault if you didn't know the situation in the caravan?

We didn't know the situation in the caravan. I didn't have a chance to stay there. . . .

So then how can you say it is your fault?

No, but I can't help but think these things when something so awful happens.

By now it had become quite obvious that even though Rita had gone along with the suggestions that she might be guilty up to a certain extent, the guilt was not an important part of her troubles. There really were no strong guilt feelings. She realized that she could not have acted any differently, for there had been no way of anticipating the fire. The aggressive feelings against her husband were also not strong enough to warrant further attention.

The fourth day of the therapy was a hard-hitting day, when Rita was forced to do a number of things she had previously considered impossible. Her therapy was progressing toward the point where a final good-bye to Beverley could be suggested. Yet when she was asked to look at a picture of her daughter, she broke down.

> *Beverley . . . oh my lovely Beverley . . . oh my lovely Beverley . . . oh my lovely Beverley . . .*
> I know it's hard.
> *Can we stop, please? Can we stop for a minute?*
> Yes.
> *I need a minute to think . . .*
> Take your time.
> *She's prettier than that. . . .*
> Now look again . . . please!
> *She had lovely big blue eyes . . . big long eyelashes, lovely hair. . . .*
> Can we look at the others as well? I haven't looked at them. I wanted your permission first.
> *Oh Momma . . . oh Momma. That's just how she was. That was the latest photograph we had ever taken at the school with Ian. My husband had these enlarged so he could look at them. . . . Oh lovely Beverley, my lovely, lovely . . . oh my lovely Beverley . . . this is how I always see her in my mind, this last photograph. . . .*
> You ought to be able to handle this now.

Yes . . . that's how she really is. That was taken in our home.

Did she have freckles?

Yes, slightly. That's her best friend there. She lives but a few blocks away. One day she had been to a wedding and left her bouquet of flowers for Beverley, and every Christmas and birthday there are always flowers from her. Her mother said that she'll never forget Beverley, and . . . that's my mother in her own home. She was a beautiful woman.

Can you describe how you are feeling now as you look at that photograph?

I wish I still had her. I think I could look at them now if I had some warning. . . . It's when things happen without warning that I am caught off balance so much. . . .

Today you have brought a photograph with you. . . .

Yes, yes . . . such a waste. . . .

Rita, we're going to hit you quite hard today. Can you take that photograph, look at it carefully and then once again say good-bye to her? Tell her that she is dead. My mother is dead! You will never see her again, you will never be able to talk to her, you will never be able to phone her again, you will never be able to discuss things with her. Once again: Say good-bye to her!

Yes, but you have had to have seen her. . . . I remember her without seeing her bandaged face. . . .

That's how she was. . . .

That's how she was . . . right!

And you will never see her again.

No . . . no. . . .

You have to go on without her. She has left you. . . . Tell her how much it hurts.

Oh it hurts so much, all the things we were going to do we will never be able to do. Never again. Oh Mom, if only you'd been able to do the things you wanted to do. If only

*you'd gotten your ruby ring. I'd have bought it for you
if I'd known. . . . My poor mom . . . my best friend
. . . I never did anything without my mom . . . she was
always there. . . .*

And now she's left you. . . .

*And now she's left me. . . . I find it so hard without you,
Mom. There's nobody to talk to anymore. I've never baked
a cake since the day you died. I got the tins out and I just
can't make a cake without you. . . . She'd buy me things,
not big things, just little things. If she knew I wanted
something, nothing was too much trouble for her. . . .*

And now tell her how much pain she's caused you by
dying. . . .

Oh I've been through hell!

Tell her how much she's hurt you. . . .

*She said she wanted to die, but oh, I didn't want her to die
. . . and she died without warning.*

She deserted you!

*She left me! She knew I didn't want her to die. She knew
how I wouldn't be able to cope with both . . . and she
died! And she left me. . . . Everybody knows I lost Beverley. But to lose my mother as well . . .*

She deserted you!

*She left me! She left me to cope on my own, and I haven't
been able to cope at all. I've been a mess since she died
. . . wandering around, not wanting to live, not wanting
to go through life without Beverley. . . .*

When you really needed her she left you. . . .

But when I really needed her she left me.

She deserted you!

She knew I didn't want her to die. . . .

But she just went ahead and died!

*She died knowing that Beverley was dead. . . . If I knew
that she was going to die I would never have told her. I am
sure she died because she knew that Beverley was dead. . . .*

And she left you to look after the mess. . . .

She left me with nothing . . . she left me with nothing. She knew I wasn't used to coping. She was always there behind me like a strong wall—and when she died, the wall just collapsed with her.

And when you needed her she wasn't there!

And when I needed her she wasn't there! How could she leave me? Why did you leave me, Mom, why did you leave me? I didn't want you to.

But she did! She left you in the lurch when you really needed her!

Why did she do that? She knew it was unbearable. . . .

And so she just left!

And so she just left. . . . I couldn't believe it. I just couldn't. I just screamed! I said to my brother, "Why is she gone? She knows I can't do without her." I felt as though I was wicked and someone was punishing me, but I haven't done anything wicked, and I just screamed, and screamed, and screamed, for I just couldn't believe it. Not her and Beverley as well . . .

Look at your mother as she was and tell her how much you relied on her; how much you needed her. Tell her how much you leaned on her, how much you needed her, how necessary she was and she just deserted you. . . .

I just couldn't go on without her, manage without her, and when I really needed her she left.

Tell her how much you hate her for that. She left you in the lurch. Left you to face the pain. Tell her how much you hate her for that. Tell her how much you hate her for the hurt she has caused you!

No! I don't hate her!

And there was indeed no hate. Bitter disappointment and a devastating sadness about having to cope without her were all that came to the forefront. The pain of not being able to see her, the aloneness, the uncertainty of having to live without the one on whom she had always been able to count was virtually tearing her to shreds—and she wanted to hold on to her. But she had come to the point where the pressure had to be increased. She was on the brink of a good-bye—a *final* good-bye.

But I still love her!
You have to send her away!
She looks much nicer than when I last saw her. . . .
You have to send her away.
I am sorry, Mom. . . . I have to manage without you. It's very hard, and you shouldn't have left me, and it would have been hard for you as well, but it would have been a little easier if I had you, but to lose you both when I needed you so much and for you to go so suddenly leaving me to cope with things I never dreamt I would have to cope with . . . the pain has been absolutely crucifying me. I hope my mother is at peace. Perhaps if you are at peace, Mom, I will get some peace too. . . .
But you have to send her away first! Then you will get some peace. Tell her to go! She chose to die! Send her away!

It was the last forceful suggestion. Suddenly it was all over.

There must be some reason why you went, Mom, when you knew I needed you so much. How to accept what you did . . . and I have to go on without you. It will be a long time before I am really able to stand on my own two feet without you always there. I have to start again without you, and try to put you aside, and not always in the front because I've got to make room for things in front; things that are here, not things that have gone! You're dead! I don't want you dead but you are dead, and I have to go on without you.

She breathed a sigh of relief, and a gentle smile began to cover her face.

She is not here anymore! She is dead now! There is still some pain but it is not as painful as it was!

Rita had said good-bye to her mother and admitted later on that she was glad she had. "I can now think of her as she was instead of torturing myself," she confessed when reviewing the progress she had made. "I thought about it a lot since yesterday, and always like this," pointing to the photograph she was holding, "Not with the burnt face."

In Rita's case, the fifth day of therapy was the crucial one, for that was the day she finally relinquished Beverley—a heart-breaking event.

The recordings and the film made of that session contain all the pathos and the agony a mother feels when she is being separated from her child forever. Deep inside, Rita already realized that the fourth day's session had been leading up to this, and when she was asked whether she had any idea as to how to proceed on this possibly crucial fifth day, she put herself totally in the hands of the therapist.

"You did what was best there with my mother," she replied trustingly, "so I leave it in your hands."

Good. Can I show you the photographs? . . . Look at it and tell yourself, "She stopped there! She will never grow any older." You will never have a daughter to do things with, to go shopping with, to talk to, to cook meals with; she will never know a boyfriend, never! She will never grow up and have children . . . you will never be a grandmother for her children.
Oh Beverley . . . I can't let her go. I can't let her go!
You've got to, Rita.
She's meant so much to us.
You've got to tell her how much she is hurting you. You've got to tell her how much pain you're feeling, and that she has to go. . . . Rita, you've got to!
She's my daughter. . . . I can't let her go, for I have so little left of her.
She left you, Rita. She left you for good. For always. She has left you!

I can't take it. . . . I can't bear it. . . . How can you say good-bye? . . .

Then talk to her. Tell her how much pain you've been in these last two years. Tell her how much agony she has caused you!

Oh Beverley . . . such a pretty name for a pretty girl. If you knew the pain that I've been in without you. The house is so quiet. . . . Of all the things we want to buy for you and we can't. . . . We're still not used to buying for one and not for two. . . . All your friends are grown up now. The boyfriends . . . all our plans . . . your daddy and I worked so hard to get you everything you wanted . . . we loved you very much and you loved us. You never went to bed with an argument. She couldn't go to sleep when she thought we were cross with her. She'd storm off to her room and slam the door, but she'd open it again and shout down, "I am sorry, Mom," and we'd be friends when she went to sleep.

You liked to give her things, didn't you?

Yes. . . .

Tell her because she's left you, you cannot give her anything more.

I can't. . . .

Tell her you can't give her anything more. Never! You have to get it through to yourself. You can never buy her anything more!

It's not fair.

You can never buy her anything more!

Oh Beverley . . .

It used to give you pleasure to give things to her, but she has left you and has taken that pleasure away from you.

I feel so frustrated! Children wanting things and parents can't afford to buy them. We could buy her anything she wanted.

But you can't buy anything for her now!

Oh . . . it's so hard. I miss her terribly. Ian's got his daddy,

*but I've got nobody; no one to choose my dresses for me
. . . I miss you terribly. For years I've cried every time
around the bus because you weren't with me. . . . Your
daddy spent hours looking out of the window in the garden, waiting for you. . . . He suffered terribly and so
have I. Every morning I wake up and realize that you're
not there. . . .*

In an attempt to show her the futility of her yearning and
the screams of anguish she uttered in her desperate longing to
hold her daughter once more, Rita was asked to explore her
reasons.

Rita, what are you screaming for? You're trying to get her
    back, aren't you?
Yes, I want her back very much. . . .
Try to call her back!
I've called and called. . . .
Try again!
Oh Beverley . . .
Try to call her back!
*Oh Beverley . . . Beverley . . . oh Beverley . . . oh I need
    you. . . . Why did you have to go like that? Why didn't
    we know? . .*
Call her back!
Oh Beverley . . .
But she doesn't come. She will never come.
*Oh we miss you so much. . . . Nana didn't want to live
    and died. . . .*
Rita, you've got to say good-bye to her NOW!
I can't, no, I can't.
You've got to, Rita. She is dead. She left you!
*It's still painful, but it feels as if I have just found her
    again!*
Rita, you will never find her like that. Tell her that she has
    to go away. You've been trying to call her back; you've been

trying to call her over, but you cannot find her. You never will!

Whenever I see a little girl with baubles in her hair I always think that could be Beverley. . . .

But you know . . . you wish that it were different, but it is not different. Look at that photograph now and tell yourself she is dead!

I don't want her to be dead!

I know, but it is so, and you have to send her away. You have to send her away.

But I can't. . . .

Tell yourself once again you will never have her as a companion to help you buy your dresses. You will never have her as a companion to cook with you. You will never be able to discuss clothing with her again or talk to her about her boyfriends.

I will never talk to her again. We had so many plans for you. You were clever, pretty—you could have done anything you wanted to. We could have helped you but we can't.

You can't do anything for her now. You cannot help her now. . . .

We can't do anything for you, my love. It's breaking our hearts. Your daddy looks at you all the time. He says you're with him all the time. Whatever we do you're always with him as you always were. . . .

Send her away, Rita!

We love you, Beverley. We don't want to send you away. Your daddy can't even mention your name. It's so painful. When he's writing in the night, he's writing it over and over again . . . Beverley-Lynn. He wanted to call you Lynn and I wanted to call you Beverley. . . . I am glad we called you Beverley because there are so many people called Lynn, and I couldn't bear it. . . .

Rita, you have to send her away!

I can't. . . .

Tell her she has to go! Tell her, "Beverley, you have to go!"

I don't want to do that!

I know, but she is dead. You cannot change it. You cannot bring her back again. You have to let her go!

Oh Beverley . . . I've got to let you go. . . . We'll always miss you. Our happy times we had . . . I hate Mother's Day because you're not here to give me my present. I hate my birthdays. You always had my present days and days in advance. She used to say, "You want to open your present tonight?" The Christmas presents she always used to open long before Christmas, and I never opened mine until Christmas morning. . . .

Rita, you have to send her away!

I can't!

She is buried! She is under the ground! And you have to turn away from her grave!

I don't want to, though!

I know you don't want to . . . but she is dead!

The session was interrupted by a walk in the hotel garden. The last few minutes had been hard on her. It was as if she felt the tearing of the ties that held her to Beverley. She needed a few minutes all alone to regain her composure. When she returned, she expressed the wish to have her husband with her during what she felt would be her final moments with Beverley. Would this support really help, or might it hinder? In a pleading voice she expressed her desperate need.

But I need him!

You have to deal with it and then the two of you can go on together. You have to do this yourself. You have to deal with it. He can't take the pain away from you and neither can I. You have to go through with it. You broke down just now when you went for a walk. . . . Go ahead . . . let go. . . . Send her away, Rita. Talk to her! Tell her that she has to go. . . . Tell her that she causes you so much pain. You have to let her go; you have to send her away!

It was more than she could take. The relentless pressure that had been applied during five therapy sessions to separate her from her dead daughter—even though it had been applied with kindness and understanding—had finally driven a wedge between them.

Her resistance faded.

> *I've got to send you away, Beverley. . . . I've got to send*
> *you away. . . . I've got to send you away. . . . I've got*
> *to send you away. . . . I've got to send you away. . . .*
> *Good-bye, my love. . . . I've got to send you away. . . .*
> *I've got to send you away. . . . I've got to send you away.*
> *. . . Good-bye, my love. . . . Good-bye, Beverley. . . .*
> *This is how I will always think of you . . . with me. . . .*
> *I will always think of you as you are now. . . . Good-bye,*
> *my love. I've sent her away! Is there anything else?*

You've done your work. I was waiting for that sigh that you have finished. How did you send her away? Could you describe it?

> *It's all very hard. Hello, my love. . . . It's been a terrible*
> *wrench. I felt as though I was being torn in two. . . . I*
> *hate to admit . . . she was gone. . . . It's very hard. . . .*
> *It clinged on and it clinged on . . . but you have to let go.*
> *It's all very painful.*

Yes, and that wound will take some time to heal, but it won't heal yet. How do you know that you've let go?

> *The pain is different.*

Can you describe it?

> *It's an empty pain . . .*

Not a sharp, biting pain?

> *No, the sharp, biting pain is gone!*

Can you think of a future now without her?

*Yes, I can. It still isn't going to be easy. I couldn't live with
it any longer. It was sheer torture. I hated to face the day.*
Can you face the day now?
*I hope so. Now I can get some peace, at last. I felt more
peaceful about my mom yesterday—and that was hard. And
now I have the same peace over Beverley.*
Is there any difference now in the way you feel—look at the
photograph now—and the way you felt this morning?
*I feel calmer . . . and slightly more detached. I was fright-
ened this morning because I knew what you were going to
make me do and I didn't think I could do it. I am more at
peace now. I don't know how to describe it. . . .*
Subjectively, how long have we been working together?
Seems like weeks . . . months. . . .
Six days! *

The next day, October 10, there was one last session with
Rita. She was ecstatic about the change. She felt like a new
woman. "I was being torn into pieces for 2½ years," she blurted
out, "and this morning . . . this morning I feel different!"

"Can we test out a few things to see whether you are really
through or not? Could you look at the photographs again?"

She looked at both her mother's and Beverley's without a
moment's hesitation and smiled a memory-filled smile.

"How about music?"

"I don't know, I haven't tried that out yet."

For a moment there was only the heavy breath of expectation and the soft rustling of a needle; and then, while Rita followed the somewhat melancholy meaning of the words in her
mind, the strains of Beverley's favorite song, "Tie a Yellow
Ribbon 'Round the Old Oak Tree," slowly filled the room.

No one moved until the entire song had been played out.
Then Rita smiled.

---

* Dr. Ramsay's reference to six days included one day during which he and
Rita discussed her case. This gathering of the "intake information" was regarded
by him as the first day of their working together.

"I was almost sick when I knew what you were going to play," she said softly, looking up. *"It's a catchy tune with very happy memories."*

While there is no doubt that Rita's bereavement has been resolved—and periodic contacts with her show that this is so—we submitted certain segments of the taped therapy session to an instrument known as the Dektor-101 Psychological Stress Evaluator, an instrument that searches for emotional stress in the human body by measuring the inaudible frequencies in the human voice.

The PSE, as the instrument is known in scientific and investigative circles, is the invention of four former employees of the Central Intelligence Agency and U. S. Army Intelligence, who decided a number of years ago to embark on a project that would enable them to evaluate electronically the conscious and subconscious sincerity of an individual's answers by measuring the rate of the basic frequencies in the human voice. The voice does not merely consist of audible frequencies—the sounds we hear—but it also contains an inaudible frequency known as a microtremor. This frequency is caused by micromuscle tremors that are totally involuntary and are affected by the stress in the human body. Vibrating at the rate of between eight and twelve beats per second, these tremors are always present and are considered to be representative of the levels of emotional stress in the body. The higher the stress, the fewer tremors there are.

The reaction of the PSE * to segments of Rita's therapy as displayed on the charts indicated right from the start that whereas her emotional stress was severe at the beginning of the therapy, it gradually diminished during the course of the sessions until toward the end of her last session it had settled down to near-normal levels.

Rita's tears had served their purpose.

Beverley was no more.

* This stress analysis was carried out by Rene Noorbergen in the United States.

CHAPTER SIX

ᵀᵀᵀᵀᵀᵀ
ᵁᵁᵁᵁᵁᵁ

The Bridge to a New Life

Is GUIDED CONFRONTATION THERAPY really *the* panacea for grief?

In many cases it is—especially when the grief has become pathological. When measured against such cases, the results of Rita's bereavement therapy are typical even though the therapy for each individual mourner will naturally develop along different lines because of individual differences.

Also people in grief therapy have been shocked to the core of their existence by a shattering experience, and they will need all the help that is available to guide them through the intricate maze of the bereavement process.

Yet not everyone passes through all the phases and components of grief, nor do all grievers experience them in the same sequence. Rita's experience, however, comes as close to an archetypical case of bereavement therapy as one can expect.

If you have selected Guided Confrontation Therapy as the method to be used to overcome your bereavement and you have met your therapist and have gone over the goals and methods that will be used in the therapy, you will naturally be anxiously awaiting the first therapy session. To cut down on the anxiety, the bereavement problem will be met head on. A brief review of the background is usually sufficient and from that point on the constructive interaction will begin.

Still, every case is different, and the question still remains, "Where to begin?"

A GENTLE INVITATION TO SHARE

During the first session the therapist will gently guide the griever into relating the entire story of the loss, right from the beginning. In many cultures, part of the ritual surrounding death is that neighbors, family members and friends keep asking to be told all the details of the death—how it happened and exactly where it happened. They want to know the smallest details, and relating the story over and over again forces the mourner to review the situation continuously.

There is much wisdom in these customs and it is usually an excellent way for the therapy to begin. Humans are unique in that they have the ability to re-create events from the past, and if the griever was benumbed at the moment of the tragedy and incapable of experiencing the real feelings that usually engulf the survivors, a directed re-creation of the sequence of events will provide her with the opportunity to relive and retrieve the hidden feelings and experience what really happened.

It will bring the dead memories back to life, and provide a sound basis for the therapy.

Don't be surprised if an invitation to share your locked-up emotions sounds like this:

". . . I said at our last session that the purpose of these meetings is to get at your feelings, so if you want to cry, do it! If you want to get angry, go ahead! Could you tell me again how he died? How you first found out about it? What happened next? Take your time—but tell me. Tell it in as much detail as you can remember. Share it!"

Often it takes just a gentle invitation to share your hurt for you to respond.

In listening to the initial story, the therapist can pinpoint the potential trouble spots and look for despair, aggression, protest or other components of the grief process. A forty-two-year-old woman, whose seventeen-year-old son had died after an unsuccessful heart operation abroad, related:

"We went to visit him on a Saturday afternoon, and after visiting hours ended at nine o'clock, my husband and I went back to the hotel for a bite to eat. At about eleven o'clock we got the message to come back to the hospital, where we were told that he had died."

Her therapist suspected that she felt guilty for having left him at such a crucial time in his life. She felt that she had abandoned him when he needed her most and went off with her husband instead.

She went on to say that since they were in a foreign country, they thought that they should return to their two daughters as soon as possible. So they went home on the Monday following the death, leaving some close friends to see to the cremation and the scattering of the ashes. Again, she felt that she had deserted him. Also, she had wanted to have the body flown home to Europe, but both her husband and the doctors had advised against this. This too caused anger against both her husband and the doctor for making her desert her son, and anger against herself for letting them talk her into it.

Needing further clarification in order to isolate the real stress point of the loss, the therapist interrupted with probing questions, forcing her to relive the situation, giving her no opportunity to avoid the painful confrontation.

"When you were telling me about standing in that room, being told by the doctor that your son was dead, you were crying just then. That is a difficult scene for you. . . . Can you tell me about it again?" he might probe, or, "I can well imagine that you feel that you deserted him that Saturday evening. You didn't know he was dying at that time, but you know it now. Can you tell me once again about your leaving the hospital after visiting hours?"

Whereas the beginning of the first session may have its own special difficulties, ending the first session is never difficult. Both parties need a breather, and a short review of what has taken place within that initial session usually provides an ideal way to end it.

"OK, Debbie," the therapist may say, "you've told me what has happened and it seems that there were several scenes that were extremely difficult for you. I think you have done enough work for one day. You did very well. I agree. What happened is something to cry about, and you need time to cry—and that's why we are here. You may feel tired for the rest of the day, but it may be rather hard to switch off in your mind what we did this morning. If you have the opportunity to go over it again at home—and if you have to cry again—do it!"

The start we have described here is ideal in many ways; it doesn't always happen that way. Let's imagine the same person but use a completely different approach, for there is always the possibility that the relating of the story will not evoke any emotional response whatsoever.

In that case, the therapist will need to introduce situations where he or she thinks a particular feeling would be appropriate and probable and discuss these with the client.

Consider this approach:

"The nurse allowed you one minute with his body after he had died before bustling you out of the room. Now, if you heard that that had happened to someone else, would it surprise you if that person became angry with the nurse? No, it wouldn't surprise you! You can really accept that on an intellectual level, can't you? You can really accept the idea that anger in that situation is a distinct possibility. But you say you can neither feel anger now nor did you at the moment of seeing your dead son's body? OK, let's go back to the situation and re-create it *not as it went, but as you would have liked it to go.*

"The nurse tells you to leave, but now you refuse. Simply refuse. You say, 'Nurse, that was my son. He's dead now, and will soon be buried. I surely deserve a little time with him. . . . I've got so little left. Please don't sent me away so soon.'

"But she did send you away. You had only one minute with him and now he's gone forever. The nurse took him away from you before you had a chance to say good-bye. If you could see that nurse again, what would you like to say to her?

"Imagine her sitting in that chair right now," he might suggest. "Look at her and tell her how you really feel. Tell her, 'You gave me so little time to be with my son. You took him away from me long before he really had to go. I wanted to be with him but you wouldn't let me . . . you took him away. You forced him out of my life!' "

Carefully designed "probes" like these are formulated to get the bereavement process going, and great care is being taken that the stressful areas are being uncovered as much as possible in the first therapy session.

Each new session always has its own unique beginning, but before long the discussion centers around what has happened since the previous visit. Questions about the "homework" you have done, inquiring about how you felt about the therapy after you left, and whether or not you have any idea as to how to proceed with the therapy will form the main part of the conversation.

Grievers are the same in one respect—and that is that when they are asked, "Where shall we begin today?" invariably the answer is, "I don't know." This means, "I know, but I am reluctant to come out with it."

The griever knows very well what is ahead and often knows how to approach the subject better than the therapist—after all, she's lived with it for a long time—but through this question she is reminded that she is an equal partner in the therapy even though she does not always take advantage of this right.

Throughout the sessions the therapist will ask questions about sensitive areas, probing for appropriate responses.

"Yesterday you found it difficult to talk about the way some of the family members behaved at the funeral," he might propose. "Can we go over that again? Let's start at the point where the car came to pick you up and you watched the other mourners. . . ."

Sometimes this works. At other times it doesn't.

REASONS FOR EVASIVE ACTIONS

Not every probe results in a promising reaction, for it is very possible that the negative emotions associated with a painful episode may have been extinguished, and this will come to the surface in the way you handle the situation. But it may also be that you have erected a mental block and are not ready as yet to allow the full impact of the loss to come through. If this is the case you won't be able to concentrate. You block, you sidetrack, and nothing therapeutic happens. We grieve at various levels, and at times a patient is ready to tackle an aspect and work it through, while at other times no amount of prompting will elicit anything worthwhile. To accept something intellectually is one thing, but the acceptance of a loss at the gut level is something entirely different. We may be able to reason things out, but when the slumbering emotions begin to stir again and memories start coming back again, the pain will once more fight for recognition, forcing the cry, "No, it just can't be!" or the anguished words, "It isn't fair," or the words, "It isn't my fault," caused by a smoldering feeling of guilt. These experiences can happen repeatedly as layer after layer of memories and feelings are uncovered.

If the patient becomes evasive and appears to sidetrack the main issues, most therapists will try other scenes and try to elicit other emotions until they finally find one that results in a meaningful response, after which the actual therapy can continue.

DENIAL IN WHATEVER FORM HAS TO BE EXTINGUISHED

Often during therapy we encounter a denial that the loss has actually occurred. Exclamations of, "I can't believe it," or, "It hasn't happened, it can't be true. I know it can't be true," are voiced by almost every griever who comes in for therapy. This is natural. There is, however, also another form of denial, and that is a total absence of feeling.

A good example of the denial of the full expression of an emotion is shown in the case of Maria, a twenty-six-year-old divorcee. Her first marriage had collapsed and had completely upset her outlook on life. Within a short time after her marital breakup she developed the idea that with two children her chances of ever getting married again were quite small, and she therefore convinced herself that she must get rid of one of them in order to improve her chances for happiness. There had been extensive fantasies of getting rid of the little boy, and eventually her feelings became very ambivalent toward the baby.

While she was in the process of developing a new relationship, the little boy became severely ill, and she soon realized that if she did not call for help he might soon die. Yet it was not until the following morning that she called her family doctor, who immediately rushed the child to the hospital in the back seat of his car. Accompanying him on the hasty ride, Maria declined to sit in the back with her sick child and instead slid into the front seat next to the doctor.

Their haste, however, was in vain, for the child died within a few hours after admission. The diagnosis? Meningitis. He would have died even if she had called for medical help the previous evening.

Shortly thereafter, she developed guilt feelings about not sitting with her little boy in the back seat of the car; about feeling happy when he died; about not calling for medical help when she realized he was critically ill; about her sense of relief when he died, enabling her to start a new life, and so on.

Soon she became tormented by guilt to the extent that she overdosed on pills and slashed her wrists. While she was in one of the institutions, a staff member told her it was stupid to feel guilt for two long years and that she was disrupting the routine of the other patients in her area with her suicidal behavior.

"OK, then I'll stop feeling guilty," she replied haughtily. "I won't try to commit suicide again, but you haven't really helped me."

Eventually she went home but this was not the solution to her problem, for the case was much more complex.

As noted, at the time of her son's death, she was just developing a new relationship. When she finally came in for therapy approximately two years later, she was three months pregnant and in dire need of attention. This greatly complicated our decision as to whether to proceed with the treatment, for in Guided Confrontation Therapy the client becomes more depressed once the therapy starts, and we did not know whether the excess stress caused by the therapy would have any detrimental effects on the unborn child. However, we knew she was suicidal, and we decided to take the chance. The alternative was to wait another six months until after the birth of the baby, but by that time she would have the complications of extra responsibilities and a postpartum depression, which in her case would be severe, possibly resulting in new suicide attempts.

Before therapy started, something happened that in our practice never happened before and hopefully will never happen again.

Before her treatment she was asked to fill out the questionnaire of the Minnesota Multiphasic Personality Inventory (MMPI) to enable us to get a comprehensive reading of her psychological condition. Combining the results of the test with the other psychological profiles and reports that were already in her file, we composed a letter to her family physician advising him that she would be accepted for treatment and enclosed the MMPI results.

Through an administrative error, the letter and the MMPI enclosures were mailed to the patient instead of the doctor, and within hours after receiving the report, Maria managed to obtain a copy of an MMPI handbook, and it wasn't long before she began to realize that the results of the test were extremely alarming. She scored very high on both the psychotic and neurotic scales and was desperately in need of psychological help. Our mistake in sending her the test results was in some ways beneficial in that it increased her awareness of the problem.

In the therapy that followed 2½ years after her son's death, it was hypothesized that guilt was still playing a vital role in her depression but that it was being inhibited.

She was asked to go back in her imagination to the conversation she had had with the staff member in the mental hospital —the one who had told her to stop feeling guilty—and get angry with him and become emotionally aroused. When she carried through on these suggestions and exploded into an outburst of anger, the therapist interrupted:

"He says it wasn't your fault, but it was! You didn't call the doctor, and it was your fault that Bobby died! You knew he was sick and you did nothing about it!"

The therapist's suggestions resulted in a massive emotional upheaval and her suicidal tendencies returned. Thanks to preventive measures, however, she was unable to act on them, and prolonged treatment with Guided Confrontation Therapy finally led to extinction of the problem to the point where she could live with the guilt and calmly say:

"I don't know if it was my fault or not, but at the time I could do nothing else."

At the customary six months' follow-up she filled out another MMPI, and all the important scales had dropped back to normal. The results were also mailed to her—but this time on purpose.

Sometime ago she called and asked what we thought of the idea of her contacting other parents who had lost children, in order to join together in a group to discuss their mutual problems. We strongly supported her in this project, and with the aid of a psychotherapist, she now counsels with groups who meet one evening per week for three months to discuss their problems and to try to work through their grief process.

Imagination also is an important tool in helping a client work through his or her bereavement. In fact, this ability to create scenes that never really happened can be very useful in concluding "unfinished business"—something a patient feels he should have done or said before the loss became a fact, yet didn't.

The mother who left her son to be cremated in a foreign country while she went home to the rest of the family was able to create in her fantasy what took place at the cremation with guiding suggestions from her therapist.

"He is no more as he was," the therapist suggested gently. "He is changed and you will have to leave him—always. Forever. You don't know exactly where he is but you have a fair idea. . . . Go out into the forest . . . climb up that hillside until you get to that place where you feel he is. Something inside you tells you, 'This is the place. This is it.' Stop, look around you . . . look at the trees, the forest, the silence, a few birds. . . . Try to have a conversation with your son. . . .

"Say to the trees, 'I've left you here in America . . . left you behind. You can't understand this at the moment, you didn't know it but I knew it. I had lots of trouble. If you could know it I think you would also understand. I left you behind . . . you have been cremated. You are not as you were before. You were my son but now you're dead. You are no more . . . and I must leave you behind. You have become a part of America, and I must give you away completely. . . .'"

Another example of vivid imagination concerns a widow who was consumed with anger toward her dead husband, but who allowed her therapist to guide her into re-creating some of the fights that had taken place before his death.

During the therapy, she was instructed to try to change the outcome of the fights so that she won instead of her former husband, to give her a feeling of victory over him instead of the memory of defeat.

In this case, the therapist's help was needed in order for her to fantasize this "fight" against her husband, but it soon became so realistic to her that she then directed all her pent-up physical anger toward the therapist. By repeating the fantasy several times, however, it finally went according to plan, minimizing the danger to the therapist, and eventually extinguishing the widow's angry memories.

DON'T UNDERESTIMATE THE POWER OF IMAGINATION

Imagination is a very useful tool in psychology and can be invaluable to the therapist not only in creating scenes but also in evoking specific emotions.

If, for example, guilt plays an important part in the emotional problems of the patient, the therapist can make use of this ability to "feel" and "see" the deceased. He may ask you, for example, to close your eyes and suggest:

"Imagine that your husband is here right now. . . . Ask him if he can ever forgive you. . . ." By making use of the deceased in this way, the guilt over what has happened in the past can finally be extinguished, and you will eventually be able to report back that you are gaining the conviction that he has forgiven you—meaning, of course, that you have forgiven yourself for your share in the disagreements.

Not all clients, however, will be able to use their feelings and fantasies to such an extent, and for those who find the "third chair" objectionable (the "third chair" is a psychological technique where the client is asked to imagine that the "other" person is present, sitting in the third chair), photographs can be a powerful substitute. In most instances the mourner bursts into tears when the pictures of the deceased are first introduced into the therapy. At home, photos may be displayed, but because viewing them can be avoided, little of the pain of grief may be experienced. However, in an actual therapy situation, this possibility of avoidance is greatly diminished, and the emotions can be more easily elicited because of Guided Confrontation Therapy.

When the first reactions begin to decrease and are obviously being extinguished, you may be asked to carry on various conversations with the photograph. In this case the therapist will have to decide which emotion is the most important at the moment.

A possible conversation for pining might be the following:

"Tell him how much you miss him. Tell him how often in the mornings breakfast isn't the same anymore; that toward six o'clock in the evening you feel the pain of knowing he won't be walking through the front door. . . . Tell him that the dinners are quiet and empty and that the food doesn't taste good anymore, that the evenings are so long, but that you don't want to go upstairs to that cold and empty bed. Tell him how long and bleak the weekends are and that you've tried to keep his garden going, but that it is now in ruins. . . . Tell him how much you miss him, how much you love him, and that your life is now so empty . . . so awfully empty. . . ."

All this you will have to address to the photograph in the hope that it will elicit various emotions associated with different situations—for eventually they will all have to be extinguished before you can be free from your sorrow.

RELEASE THE LINKING OBJECT

Since the various emotional components of grief may surface at various points throughout the therapy, it is never possible to plan sessions with the extinguishing of certain negative emotions in mind, but sometime during one of the sessions, the therapist will ask his patient to explore her mind for the presence of "linking objects." These can be records, ties, hats, letters, pens, jewelry—anything that belonged to the deceased. The psychologist V. D. Volkan described these aptly as "objects that are typically treasured by people unable to resolve their grief—something that magically provides the illusion of communication with the dead. The pathological mourner can control this illusionary communication, turning it on by musing over the object and turning it off by putting the object out of sight in an inaccessible place."[1]

Sometimes the object is touched, as was the case with the patient who had hidden the top of her little girl's pajama underneath the bed and hugged the pajama top and smelled it just before she went to sleep at night, so as to have one quiet moment of communion with her deceased baby daughter. Quite often, however, the object is never touched, for to many the knowledge that it is available appears to be sufficient.

One Jewish woman whose parents had been killed in Nazi concentration camps during the war had a pendant containing a photo of her mother and kept it in a drawer for more than thirty years, never touching it. When it was explained to her what a "linking object" was and how it can still tie the survivor to the deceased, she immediately understood and promised to bring the pendant with her to the next therapy session.

It cost her many hours of indecision and pain before she finally decided to handle and open the pendant, but at the next session she beamed proudly as she showed the photograph that had been hidden inside all those years.

Another patient, a film producer, had forty-five hours of film of his wife and daughter, which he had locked in a closet when his wife divorced him. When he entered therapy to overcome the trauma of his loss, the film had been untouched for approximately ten years.

These instances of absolute surrender to the realization of real progress in their therapy can be moments of incomparable victory, but often they come at the end of a chain of emotional lows where the outward expressions of their inner turmoil are often painful to watch.

Some of the patients who go through Guided Confrontation Therapy scream out their anger, pain and frustration; others curl up like wounded animals and moan softly, staring at the walls with a forlorn look in their eyes. Still others shake and tremble, looking around them with eyes filled with fear and agony, while still others just sit there, rocking back and forth, back and forth, unable to verbalize their sadness; and there are still more who just pace around the room, wringing their hands or biting their fingernails nervously.

The last emotional component to appear during the therapy is aggression against the dead person. He died and is at rest, but the mourner remains in pain and is burdened with the problems of his or her intense bereavement. It is not certain, however, whether this aggressive element is found in all cases of bereavement—especially if the deceased was a child—but the therapist must consider its existence a possibility, for if aggression is present and is not dealt with, the last important step cannot be taken.

Every therapist has his own way of leading up to the end of his therapy, and inasmuch as our approach is very direct, since that produces the best results, we maintain and advocate this method through the final session.

Example:

"Take another good look at that photograph! Look at him! Tell him how much misery and pain he has caused you. Tell him that he has left you in the lurch; that he deserted you. That he has wrecked your life because he died! Tell him you hate him for deserting you. Tell him!"

LETTING GO, THE HARDEST STEP IN THE FINAL PHASE OF THERAPY

This aggression is often combined with the last important step in the therapy—that of "letting go" of the deceased. The griever must eventually relinquish the lost person before new ways of life can be found in which the deceased does not play a major role. The mother must say farewell to her child before she can entertain the idea of having another baby; the young widow must say farewell to her dead husband before she can even think of marrying again. The man who has lost his job must cease to be an emotional cripple before he can become a success in his new position, and even the blind wife must say a final good-bye to her dead husband before she can ever trust anyone else to be her eyes.

This leave-taking is very difficult. "Listen" to the therapist talk to his patient, helping her take leave from her dead daughter, the child she treasured more than anything else in life.

The time has come, Mary. The time for parting has come. You've got to let her go. . . .

But I can't . . . I can't let her go . . . She belongs to me. . . .

Mary, you've got to.

I can't. . . . I can't. . . . She's my only daughter. . . . I can never have another one . . . and already I have so little left of her. . . .

You have to face it, Mary. She has left you for good. She has left you for always and she is never coming back . . . never!

There is no way I can take leave of her. . . . She is my pretty little girl. . . . The thought of leaving her kills me . . . it tears my heart apart. I can't say farewell to her. . . . She's my life. . . .

You don't have to be blunt about it but you *have* to do it. Just talk to her and make her understand. . . .

Oh my honey . . . this is such a hard moment. . . . Everything has gone wrong since you left us. . . . Our lives have fallen apart. . . . We cry day and night, always. . . . Everything centered around you, and you are gone now and have taken all our joy with you. You were so beautiful . . . so lovely. . . . you are the love . . . you are what we always wanted and now you're down there and I can't even touch you. . . .

The agony that accompanied these words cannot be described. Yet these inner feelings had to be verbally expressed before they could be extinguished. This "letting go" of the lost object or person is not only very difficult but also nearly impossible, both emotionally and technically. Most grievers are terrified of approaching this point. "Once we've gone through that, we will have nothing left," many of them remark, and there is indeed a lot of truth in this. They will have nothing left of the past in which the lost object played a major role. Some carry it a step farther and argue outright that if they really "let go" they will be losing an integral part of themselves, inasmuch as the deceased was "one" with them.

This is true up to a point, but there will be enough of the *real* person left after the "letting go" to reconstruct a new life.

Grievers also fear that if they let the therapist guide them through this phase, even the images and memories of the departed will disappear and that they will never again be able to remember what the past was like or what "they" did together.

This, of course, is totally untrue, for Guided Confrontation Therapy cannot take your memory away from you. You will get him back again, but this time in another form, in another way, in a memory without pain and without agony.

People often think of the "letting go" as too passive a process and don't know how to handle it, but sending the dead person away forever is actually an active deed and has to be combined with a certain degree of aggression. It has to be absolute and complete if the process is to be resolved and the griever can finally move into the reintegration stage.

The final good-bye has to be said—and this cannot be conditional.

One patient was asked to take leave of her mother. After spending a restful five minutes with her eyes closed, she reported that she had done it.

When after a brief moment she was asked to explain exactly *how* she had done it, she replied,

"I said, 'Bye for now.'"

Her choice of words clearly implied a temporary separation and not a final and definite good-bye. After this was pointed out to her, she could immediately see that this had not been a real good-bye but rather an *auf wiedersehen*. A long and painful upheaval ensued before she finally reached the stage where the actual separation could take place.

One of the most difficult things to do in grief therapy is to ascertain that the final leave-taking has indeed occurred, and you may be assured that if you have not been involved in an obvious emotional struggle, you will not as yet have reached the point of total separation. One of the signs that you really have let go of the deceased is that you feel completely spent, exhausted and empty. If you don't feel this way during what you think is the end of that phase, then both you and the therapist should retrace your steps and go through the process all over again. There are occasions when the mourner becomes angry with the therapist, and most psychologists recognize that this is a sign that the patient has not reached the end but that the psychologist is indeed on the right track, for this type of a reaction is usually a sign that the patient feels that the loved one is being taken away from her forever.

There is no need to deal with this anger except to allow time for it to be extinguished, but when it does occur, it's better to end the session.

Still the question: How do you know you have really reached the end of your grief and are ready to move on into the reintegration phase of your bereavement and are once again becoming "one" with your surroundings?

It was not until the thirteenth session that the woman whose son had died of a heart operation managed to say a final goodbye to her boy, but in a way that was totally unexpected.

Photographs shown to her had been of no avail until the first ten minutes of the thirteenth session. Quietly she began to recall how they had enjoyed their first few days in the United States by visiting New York and Washington and how they had enjoyed seeing the sights of the capital.

"I let my mind drift back to those days in Washington," she mused softly, "and how we stood on the Capitol steps looking out at the Washington Monument. It was a beautiful sight. But as we started walking down the steps, I stumbled and he grabbed my arm. He gave me strength just when I needed it."

She paused for a moment and sighed.

"And you know . . . that's where I let go of him while he

was still alive and still well and still strong.

"We walked down the steps together, and in my mind as I turned away he went on into the wilderness, away into the distance. He was going away and I didn't turn back.

"In that way I let go of my son."

She was able to put her leave-taking into words, but most people don't. Some can describe the change, but others close up completely. Those who do talk about it will admit that they feel as if a weight has been lifted off them.

"I can finally breathe again," one patient remarked. Another commented after the final "letting go": "The world is once more in color. I can look around me now and see things as they really are." One even confessed that the deceased no longer stood in front of her, blocking her every thought and action, but that he had finally stepped aside so that she was free to move forward. The change is often dramatic and obvious but not recognizable until the point has been reached.

If objects that in the past evoked severe emotional reactions, such as looking at photographs, listening to the deceased's favorite music or handling a linking object, no longer elicit negative reactions, then you have moved safely through the therapy and are well on the way to reintegration.

But—and here's a word of warning—Guided Confrontation Therapy probes deep into the emotional makeup of the individual and may trigger other unresolved conflicts from the past, either during the treatment or shortly thereafter.

A number of years ago, someone came to our office suffering from a severe case of agoraphobia to the point that he was becoming a total invalid. It was not until the very last treatment session that the underlying problem finally surfaced.

"I don't know why I am telling you all this," he suddenly blurted out, "because I have never told anyone about this before, but my father was a collaborator with the Germans during the German occupation of the Netherlands, and when the kids at school found that out, I became a virtual outcast."

The episode he referred to had taken place more than thirty

years prior to his coming into therapy, but he sensed a connection and asked for help.

"I was an outcast for years," he said, embittered, "and even though I never agreed with him I could never really get angry with him either."

Since his father's treason had affected the relationship with both his father and his fellow classmates, it was decided to finish off the "unfinished business" with the schoolchildren first. But finally he did get emotional, and did fight back—even though in his imagination—and vented all his anger at the children.

Jubilantly he went home, only to return the next day.

"It's really my father," he confessed. "It's my relationship to him that bothers me."

Guided Confrontation Therapy finally helped him settle his affairs and disagreements with his father, and after thirty long years, he decided to let his father go; let him die, and rest—forever.

Reports that reached us months later indicated that the therapy and his new grip on life had practically changed his personality overnight. Previously he had been most demure and inhibited at company staff meetings. Now his aggressive attitude was almost unbearable. His former anxiety at staff meetings had been based on his reluctance to fight back against the children who had pestered and teased him thirty years ago, and this had affected his consequent behavior. He had not dared to be aggressive at the company because at school he had never fought back.

In talking with people who have gone through GCT to solve their loss trauma, one impression seems to stand out above all else, and that is that Guided Confrontation Therapy is a working relationship between patient and therapist that is based on mutual respect, understanding and a close bond of emotional attachment. But since the former griever is always glad the ordeal is over, the bond is never hard to break.

In the end, no matter how much agony and pain has been elicited, the griever—now the ex-griever—gradually pulls away with a feeling of indescribable relief. The partnership, which was based on sadness and human misery, now dissolves amid feelings of happiness and relief.

It is ended, yet the former griever knows instinctively that it is always possible to return for help and a shoulder to lean on should the memories of the past return or become too strong.

There is never a final good-bye to grief, for grief really knows no end. It simply softens and is absorbed within the routine of life, and when the touches of pain flow back against the tide of memory, they will not be felt as the remainders of the great loss of long ago, but rather as indications that we are still alive, for grief and life cannot be separated.

CHAPTER SEVEN

GCT, the Modern Method
That Heals Both Mind and Body

FOR THOSE WHO HAVE BEEN searching for a hope-giving therapy, Guided Confrontation Therapy is like a breath of fresh air.

When it was first developed at the University of Amsterdam's Phobia Clinic, it was aimed at solving the bereavement problems connected with death, but soon it was found to be effective in curing grief caused by other losses as well.

Loss of homeland, loss of job, loss of pride, loss of position, rape and loss from surgery can now all be treated under the expanding umbrella of Guided Confrontation Therapy. *In fact, wherever there is a traumatic experience caused by loss—and the loss does not have to be physical but can also be of a psychic nature—this form of therapy can be used, often with great success.*

FINANCIAL LOSS

To many people, our twentieth century has become the "age of enlightenment," but few care about the niceties of life if they are plagued by unemployment, depression, bankruptcy, or the whims of either employer or labor unions. We place a high value on work, on having a sound economic basis with which to support our lifestyle, but the inability of our society to provide job security and lifestyle stability is placing increasing pressure on the employed segment of the population—and the results are often disastrous.

People find themselves in a double bind; on one hand, it's important and gratifying to work; yet on the other, this source of pride can be taken away without as much as a moment's notice.

People who experienced the economic crash of 1929 and the resulting lean years of the 1930s will remember the reports about the economic and financial giants who lost their fortunes. Many business empires diminished to nothing in a matter of hours. Within a short period, the lives of successful entrepreneurs and upper-class merchants were transformed from affluence to poverty, reducing their self-image to zero.

And the same problems are still with us today.

Social scientists have studied the correlation between death and unemployment ever since the Great Depression, and their forecasts for the years following the depression of the late 1970s and early 1980s are grim.

Dr. M. Harvey Brenner, associate professor of hygiene and public health at Johns Hopkins University in Baltimore, has pointed out that traditionally the stress patterns rise during periods of depression, and that this trend is not only realistic but is also measurable and predictable.

Based on a detailed analysis of death rates and unemployment rates in the United States over a one-hundred-year period, *he predicts that the economic slump of the early 1980s will result in a decided increase in murder, suicide, cardiovascular disease, alcoholism and other death-causing diseases.*

Quoted in an Orlando *Sentinel Star* newspaper interview dated August 19, 1980, Dr. Brenner warns:

"For every 1 percent increase in unemployment, there could be an additional 38,886 deaths throughout the country over a six-year period—and nobody is immune." [1]

In a study he conducted for the Congressional Joint Economic Committee, Dr. Brenner estimates that the fatalities will begin to show up two or three years after the initial downturn.

"Even when people are able to get jobs again," he points out, "if they are over thirty-five, they often experience a paradoxical decline in social position and self-esteem. The vision here is of individuals, expelled from the economy, who attempt to reintegrate themselves and, oddly enough, lose further."

Another study prepared by the University of Michigan suggests that the problems of the unemployed may actually be only the tip of the iceberg, because its effects are not limited solely to the actual unemployed but to their families as well. Using the implications of Dr. Brenner's study and taking into account the vast number of unemployed in the state of Michigan during the early 1980s, that state alone could have an estimated additional nineteen thousand deaths over the next six-year period—all stress-related.

"We do have the correlation now between death rates and unemployment," voices Jeanne Gordus, assistant research scientist at the University of Michigan's Institute of Labor and Industrial Relations in Ann Arbor, Michigan. "We don't know when the deaths will occur, but unemployment triggers it. The timebomb is set off." [2]

Taking the Holmes and Rahe Social Readjustment Rating Scale as basis, the complications of being unemployed (fired at work, change of financial state, change in number of arguments with spouse, change in living conditions, change in recreation, and change in social activities) pile an additional 182 Life Crisis Units on those already accumulated, placing the unemployed wage-earner in a much higher health-risk bracket, thus adding weight to the expectation that the economic slump of the 1980s will lead to a noticeable increase in the number of unnecessary deaths.

Can these deaths be prevented?

Depression does play a major role in the aftermath of losing a job, but there is more to it than just that.

Let's take a look at a patient who came into our office a number of years ago. He was highly intelligent, a professional in his field, but had been severely depressed for about two years. His extreme anxiety was making him suicidal. Even though now gainfully employed, the feeling that his depression was related to the way he had left his former employer was something he couldn't get out of his mind.

He had not felt any aggression or resentment when he was fired, even though the circumstances surrounding his leaving were sufficient to make him angry, but there was nevertheless an uneasy feeling.

As soon as the therapy for his depression began, the latent aggression shot to the surface. Extremely agitated and bristling with anger, he described how in his imagination he was trying to get even with the chairman of the board. Slowly, meticulously, the patient vented his anger by taking his knife, cutting the chairman to pieces. First his fingers, then his hands, next his arms, his legs, his head, and finally his genital organs were carefully severed from his body. In fact, the patient's imagination became so lively during one point in the therapy session that it became necessary to remind him of the rule stating that a patient is not allowed to "damage" the therapist!

Once the anger was out into the open, it was soon followed by the expected grief reaction.

"Yes, it *was* a good job, and I *am* sorry I lost it! My own fault, I guess. I really didn't want to leave the company but I was forced out. Fired!" And suddenly all the hidden feelings of despondency, grief, guilt, anger, shame, jealousy and remorse came to play their part. What had started as treatment for depression became Guided Confrontation Therapy for grief all over again—only this time the principles were used in eliciting responses that had a direct bearing to grief caused by the loss of a job.

LOSS OF COUNTRY

Another area to which this therapy can be applied is that of refugees and political exiles—that is, all those who for one reason or another had to leave their homeland under pressing circumstances and were forced to relocate among people of a different culture.

It is an age-old problem that is once again gaining prominence because of the smoldering wars in the Far East, the political oppression in Eastern Europe and the political unrest in other parts of the world.

A refugee faces a number of unique losses. He is not only forced to adjust to a new culture, but generally there is also a loss of relatives, a loss of the "old way of life" and of possessions. Accompanying this are feelings of hopelessness, uselessness, despair, anger, vengeance, suspicion, desertion, anguish, anxiety and loneliness. Those who escape from Eastern Europe are often treated as equals in the West. Even though their physical and psychic losses may be just as real as those of other refugees, they fuse easier with nationals of Western countries because of similarities in culture. Yet these refugees are still lonely and sad.

The refugees coming to the West from the Far East—for example, Vietnam, Laos, and Cambodia—are not just exposed to all the traumatic experiences that are part of their existence, but they face the effects of a severe culture shock as well. The green hills of home are no longer theirs; the saffron robes of the Buddhist monks, the soft-spoken gentleness of the hill people, the genteel lifestyle of Southeast Asia have faded out, together with their smiles. Their vacant, soulless eyes stare in utter bewilderment at their newfound home, yet they don't understand. They have been mauled ruthlessly by the devastating power of war; have been mangled by the trauma of escape, refugee camps, starvation, airlifts and eventual transplantation into an alien land where their old way of life never existed and where they never will be understood. They have exchanged the horrors of war and the bloodied surroundings of home for the tranquillity of the soap opera and the lonely life of the exile, and somehow they still wonder why.

To many refugees their newly adopted home is in the beginning usually no more than a new existence in more comfortable surroundings. Their past has actually *died*, and only "an active taking leave" of the past, followed by a sincere endeavor to integrate themselves into their newly found culture, can restore some measure of meaning to life.

THE TRAUMA OF RAPE

In a 1975 exploration of rape, *Against Our Will*, author Susan Brownmiller begins one of her chapters in a very matter-of-fact way.

"Women are trained to be rape victims," she writes. "To simply learn the word 'rape' is to take instruction in the power relationship between males and females. To talk about rape, even with nervous laughter, is to acknowledge a woman's special victim status. We hear the whispers when we are children: *Girls get raped.* Not boys. The message becomes clear. Rape has something to do with our sex. Rape is something awful that happens to females: It is the dark at the top of the stairs, the undefinable abyss that is just around the corner, and unless we watch our step it might become our destiny." [3]

This is a hard introduction to an undeniable act of savagery. Men can read or hear about it; but women are more aware of the fear and terror that accompany the very sound of the word "rape," for of all the contacts between male and female, the forcible subjugation of a woman's body for illegitimate sexual purposes is still considered to be one of the most hideous examples of sadistic behavior.

Rape is legally defined as sexual intercourse with a woman under conditions of force or threat of violence. Ever since the famed Code of Hammurabi was chipped on a seven-foot column of diorite stone about four thousand years ago, outlining punishments for various crimes *including* rape, it has been regarded as a serious crime. In fact, it is still punishable by death in sixteen states of the United States and is punishable by twenty years to life in prison in twenty-seven other states. Between 1930 and 1948, 316 men were executed for rape in the United States, not to mention the many who have been executed for committing rape in the Middle East under Islamic law.

Although the exact incidence of rape is unknown, it has been estimated that the rate is between twenty-eight and seventy victims per one hundred thousand women per year, with the actual rate being two to four times higher than the number of cases reported. Most rapes are not brought to the attention of the authorities because of the social stigma involved and the additional trauma suffered by the victim.[4]

The reported incidence of rape has increased dramatically since the 1960s.[5] One of the reasons for this may be that the victims are more willing to come forward and press legal charges. The fact that special rape crisis centers are now available to counsel those who have been raped may also be a contributing factor to why more cases are being reported. Furthermore, supportive procedures have been developed to help the rape victim adjust to her traumatic experience and even to aid her legally.[6]

There is indeed a place for crisis centers staffed by people who are experts in meeting the emotional upheaval of rape victims. Once assaulted, they are often traumatized by the experience, both mentally and physically. The rape itself can leave a psychological mark on a woman for many years afterward, giving her a negative attitude toward her sexual relationship with her husband.[7]

There is no such thing as a "typical" rape case history, but the case of Sally H. contains many of the components that are characteristic of forcible rape. The following paragraphs based on her intake interview give a glimpse into the trauma that disrupted an innocent human life.

"I'd been working my shift at the shoe store and had stayed behind for a while," she started hesitantly, "and when I finally walked to my car in the parking lot across the street it was about ten at night. I had no reason to worry, for nothing had ever happened to me, and this time nothing happened either. I will have to admit that the thought that someone might be lurking behind my car had occurred to me, but there was no one, and there was no one in my back seat either, so I got in and drove off.

"I had gone about two blocks when one of the boys I knew from a previous job crossed the street and when I stopped to say hello he asked me for a ride. So I let him in on the driver's side, and he started driving.

"At first he talked. Then suddenly he began to beat me with his fist and told me to lay down while he kept driving. He forced me down on the front seat and kept his fingers on my throat. I could hardly breathe, and I began to cry. . . . There was nothing I could do, for every time I tried to move my head, he'd loosen his grip and beat me again, so I stayed quiet until we got to the edge of town. He stopped the car behind a cluster of trees and yanked the car door open, pulled me out and forced me down on the grass.

" 'I wanted you for a long time,' he hissed excitedly, 'and this time I am gonna make you.'

"He pulled my slacks down and before I knew it, he was inside of me. Sweat was pouring down his face while he did it, and he was saying the dirtiest words. I couldn't do a thing. He had my arms pinned down. I thought, 'Oh God, please get this over with . . . don't let him kill me.'

"I must have passed out, for when I got up it was much later. He had gotten up and said, 'I'll take your car and leave it in the parking place near where you work. Don't ever tell on me . . . I'll have my buddies kill you.'

"I got partially dressed and began walking down the road when a police car picked me up.

"Ever since that time I don't dare to go out with a boy anymore. When I see someone with a beard I begin to shake. Whenever I see a Ford station wagon I begin to cry and want to run away. I have sold my car since but I used to own a Ford. I was brought up in a nice Baptist family—my father is a lay preacher—and I can't tell them what happened because they won't understand. They'll blame *me* for what happened. I always wanted to remain a virgin until I got married, and now this has happened I will never get married. Which boy will want me now?

"It's been two years now since it happened . . . and I wonder if I will ever be the same again. I am so ashamed. . . . Maybe if I just try to forget it, it will go away. I still worry about it day and night, and lately I can't sleep because of it. I see it happen all over again—every night. . . . Do you think it will ever go away?"

A careful comparison of rape case histories shows that even though forcible rape reactions vary greatly from victim to victim, most victims regard rape as a highly traumatic experience, *one that bears a close resemblance to the phases and components of grief caused by death, as shown in Chapter Three.**

In "death grief" we are dealing with the trauma caused by the loss of a human being, someone who was loved and cherished. In a case of rape we are also dealing with a loss, and even though in some instances it may involve loss of virginity, the loss due to rape is in reality much more complex than that. Rape may indeed be a loss of virginity, but it also signifies a loss of self-esteem, a loss of pride, a loss of self-worth, a loss of self-assuredness and a loss of independence. The rape victim's reliance on others suddenly becomes stronger, and whether she resolves the painful and disruptive aftereffects of the rape in her own way or seeks therapeutic intervention, she will eventually come to the realization that the tranquillity of her life has been interrupted to such an extraordinary degree that she will never really be the same again.

Guided Confrontation Therapy is not the only answer to the emotional problems created by rape, but its flexibility surely makes it one of the most effective therapies available.

---

* See the Appendix under "Rape Trauma" for additional guidelines.

LOSS FROM SURGERY OR ACCIDENT

The loss of one of the vital senses or a part of the human body is another area where Guided Confrontation Therapy can be helpful.

Someone who has lost a limb, or whose hearing, seeing or feeling has permanently been impaired, or who is forced in some way to stop functioning as a whole human being feels loss just as deeply as one who is suffering from bereavement due to death. Any loss of a part or a sense of the human body is traumatic, for it signifies a final separation from something that was indispensable up to that point, and when this "something" is lost, you are no longer the same.

While every physical loss is dramatic, few losses are as shattering as the removal of a woman's breast as the result of breast cancer. In 1980, 405,000 people will die of cancer in the United States alone, or about one every seventy-eight seconds, with 109,000 of these cases resulting from breast cancer. One out of eleven women will develop breast cancer at some point during their lives, 19 percent of those who develop it will die and many who do survive will need psychological therapy. *But there is hope, for the five-year survival rate for breast cancer has already climbed to 85 percent, while the incidence of the disease has remained rather constant.*

A number of years ago, the Gallup Organization, Inc., conducted a survey with startling results. The survey, which was launched in 1974, revealed several misconceptions about cancer.

Only 12 percent of all the women polled were aware that not every lump in the breast means cancer, and—as if we were still living in the Middle Ages—an amazing 62 percent still believed that breast cancer could be caused by a severe blow to the breast. Because of these and other erroneous ideas, only 18 percent of those polled practiced monthly breast self-examinations, while 46 percent openly admitted that this type of examination would only increase their worry.[8]

As part of her doctoral thesis for the University of Amsterdam, Abeel van Voorst Vader conducted a detailed study comparing the bereavement process caused by death to that caused by "loss of breast" and raised some interesting questions.

Why, for example, is the female breast so important in our society? What is the significance of the female form to both men and women? What does the loss of a woman's breast mean to the other members of the family? How will it influence the emotional life of the victim? And why is the loss of a breast more traumatic than, let's say, the loss of a hand or an arm, which is really more needed in daily life?

First, in our culture the female breast is a prime symbol of femininity, and often its size and form determine a woman's sex appeal.[9] Also, for many women the breasts are the determining factors for their status, security and standing among their peers.[10] Breasts are major sources of sexual pleasure, and because they are also a natural life-support system for the offspring, they fulfill a vital physical as well as a symbolic role in the life of a woman. They are so important that some have even compared the loss of a woman's breast to the loss of a man's penis.[11]

Because of these factors, the removal or even the mere *threat* of removal of one or both breasts due to cancer is nearly always regarded by the woman involved as a terrifying experience. What makes the threat of breast cancer even worse is the stark realization that cancer is an illness that can eventually lead to death—and an extremely painful death at that. Even though both mastectomies and hysterectomies are considered major surgery, the very fact that the uterus is hidden and the breasts are visible places the removal of a breast in a completely different light. It is not just that something is being done to one of the sexual areas of the female body that makes a mastectomy different from other operations; it is also the outward feminine aspects of the female breasts combined with their psychological value that make this operation so emotionally charged.[12]

In the research conducted in Amsterdam, attention was focused on two important variables that appeared to play a vital role in the psychological acceptance of a mastectomy: *the age of the patient* and her *physical "investment" or appearance.*

The age at which the mastectomy takes place is of great psychological importance, and the operation is more shocking *before* than *after* menopause.

The sexual significance of the breasts as well as the motherly role they can play are much greater before menopause, but after a woman passes through the change of life, these factors change. The most problematic psychological complications in connection with this operation can be expected *during* menopause, since the loss of fertility and the diminishing mother-role has already placed the woman in a very vulnerable position. And when a mastectomy is performed on younger women and those who are still single and without children, they will undergo a more severe emotional shock than those who are married and have children.[13] Women under forty-five years of age generally consider their adjustment to a mastectomy less successful than older women and feel a greater need to seek professional therapy for psychological problems.[14] Yet women who experience a breast removal during their menopause suffer more from deep depressions [15] than those over sixty years of age, who complain more about their physical discomfort than about their emotional disturbances.[16]

The physical "investment" a woman has in her outward appearance can also have a decided influence on how she reacts to a mastectomy. To some women physical appearance and sexual appeal are of prime importance, and the idea of losing a breast can damage their emotional stability. In fact, the more a woman equates her self-image with her outward appearance and the greater pride she has attached to the size and shape of her breasts, the higher the chances are that her surgery may lead to psychological complications.

The discovery of a sudden lump in one of the breasts can be a terrifying experience. This fear increases steadily—first when her family physician advises her to see a specialist, and afterward, when the decision is made to be admitted to a hospital for an exploratory operation. Filled with apprehension, she enters the hospital and feels herself wheeled into the operating room, where the doctors responsible for her survival await her.

A woman knows that if there is a mastectomy, her life and entire future will undergo a dramatic change.

Is it any wonder that when she awakens in the recovery room and discovers that both her breasts are still there that she is even more apprehensive? Is the lump indeed benign, or is she so filled with cancer that they just sewed her up again? It is a terror that gradually subsides even after she is told that there was no cause for alarm.

But what about the patient who wakes up and realizes that her worst fears have become reality? She has lost something— a part of her body—and this physical change will alter her future forever. Within a few hours she has become "different"; she has changed. Lying there, bewildered, she wonders if everyone will notice that she only has one breast. She may perhaps feel mangled, disfigured, grotesque—and even unwanted. In her case the surgeon's knife has struck far beyond mere flesh. He has cut deep into the psyche of a defenseless woman, and only time will tell how well she survives.

While some of the uncertainty is gone, she will still have to adjust to the idea of having lost a breast, but with this knowledge comes the added realization that cancer has actually invaded her body and that the fear of succumbing to this loathsome intruder will always be with her.

The first days following the surgical intervention are known as the "days of cloudy painfulness," when most patients are still somewhat benumbed and in a state of shock,[17] but once this misty feeling disappears, many conflicting emotions come crashing down. This is the time when the emotions of fear and uncertainty begin to take hold and start paving the way for a growing feeling of depression.

What are her chances of escaping a severe postmastectomy depression? Is it possible to identify a "high risk" group—that is, women who, because of their manner and degree of psychological adjustment, have placed themselves in a category of people who will not be able to resolve their bereavement without professional intervention?

There is such a group, but fortunately most mastectomized women do not need extensive therapeutic help after their often unexpected ordeal. Various statistics taken from both sides of the Atlantic indicate that many of the patients can draw upon their own inner resources to bounce back into a full, productive life within a reasonable period of time. *Our concern is with those women who are not able to cope by themselves with their new situation and for whom a deep depression is becoming a way of life.*

Information gathered from interviews with mastectomized patients one year after their operation and released in 1978 shows that 25 percent of them needed professional psychological help to overcome their fear or depression, while another 35 percent admitted to having serious sexual difficulties.[18] Using the figure of 109,000 mastectomies per year as basis, this means that roughly 25,000 to 38,000 *patients per year* feel the need for therapeutic help—a disturbing figure indeed.

Predicting the outcome of a psychological shock is not a main concern of psychology, even though many of the tests used in the profession lean in that direction. However, this does not mean that the recorded observations made by clinical psychologists during their follow-up consultations with their patients may not be used as indicators of trends.

A two-year follow-up study, the results of which were published in 1977,[19] focuses attention on a number of "high risk" categories—that is, women in whom the tendency toward psychological complications were recognizable even before the surgery.

- Women who are having surgery during, immediately after or prior to menopause will probably develop psychological problems that are sexually oriented.

- Women who show clear signs of depression just before the operation—aside from previous psychiatric disturbances—will probably develop depressive symptoms for which medical or psychological therapy will be required.
- Women who before the operation score high for emotional instability on the Eysenck Personality Inventory Neuroticism Scale may remain tense about the loss following surgery.

Abeel van Voorst Vader adds further factors for consideration:

- Women whose outward appearance forms the basis for their emotional security.
- Women whose roles in life have become highly problematic—factors that often occur during their change of life.
- Women who are young and unattached and who are unable to count on much emotional support.
- Women with extreme anxiety about illness and death.

Of course, the question arises: What can a woman do to help herself?

Back at home she may swing from one end of the emotional scale to the other, trying to adjust to a new life. Yet while she will *want* to adjust, some of the obstacles may seem so insurmountable that she may just consider suicide as a viable alternative.

To pull through she will need *much energy*. But both body and psyche cannot draw from an inexhaustible supply; the energy must be reserved for the actual physical healing process and not wasted on unnecessary worry. This, however, does not always occur. Some patients take as many as eight years after the operation to get over their loss—and even then, the process is not finished.[20]

To protect yourself against severe bereavement, remember these points:

EXAMINE YOUR FEELINGS CAREFULLY

The phases and components of loss grief are almost identical to those of death grief as described in Chapter Three. If any of the phases and components described, such as disorganization, searching behavior, shame, desolate pining and guilt should bear a resemblance to the feelings or actions experienced, then that specific phase or component has not as yet been experienced.* If it is anger, vent it; if it be jealousy, express it. Find a close confidante who will be understanding but firm, and use her as a sounding board to discuss and examine your feelings. Flush them out! Work with each elicited emotional component until it slowly diminishes. Total extinguishment of each phase is needed before the first step can be taken on the road to health.

DRAW STRENGTH FROM YOUR FAMILY

The family is unique, and its value and importance should never be underestimated. In a successful and harmonious marriage, every problem should be shared, and this includes all those connected with a serious medical crisis such as a mastectomy.

Facing your partner with a plea for help and understanding may be difficult, but it must be done and it can be done. You may not be aware that when you passed through your own physical crisis, your husband experienced a crisis of his own. His anger, worry, helplessness, concern, growing anxiety and anguish put him in a critical psychological state. Feelings of shock, disappointment, fear and sorrow are not yours alone. He, too, feels them in a real way. His worry for the future is just as strong as yours, and the anger in his voice does not indicate

---

* See the Appendix under "Mastectomy Grief" for additional guidelines.

a fading love for you, but is rather a groan of desperation for not being able to resolve this menacing crisis.

He, too, has a need to express himself. It is at this point that both patient and partner will have to share their sorrows and worries and start planning to erase the past in exchange for future happiness. The psychological tension that has been building up within and between you has to find release, and only a mutual airing of anxieties can be the start of this process.

EMBARRASSMENT

There simply is no way that this feeling can be avoided in the loss-bereavement process. It may be a natural impulse to turn away from your husband when undressing, but you will have to face the reality of the new situation eventually—so why not now? It has been suggested that "systematic desensitization" —where both patient and husband look at the scar together and possibly dress the wound together—should be considered, for the partner must be brought into the process of acceptance.

Once the shock has worn off for both, the emotion of shame or embarrassment will begin to fade. An open relationship like this will eliminate the "need" to change clothes in the dark or dress behind locked doors and may also aid in the re-establishment of normal sexual relations, as this is considered to be the central point in the solution of relevant psychological problems.

COMMUNICATE! TALK ABOUT WHAT HAPPENED

Cancer is a subject most people would rather avoid discussing, especially with someone who has just undergone major surgery. And when the postmastectomy patient feels ashamed or embarrassed about her loss and consciously avoids all contact with those around her—family, friends, neighbors, colleagues, etc.—the subject *will* remain hidden. The dormant emotions will not be vented or given a chance to be extinguished. Not sharing the anguish, pain, sorrow, anxiety and concern is in itself a form of denial, a component that plays a major role throughout the bereavement process. *There has to be a sharing, an opening up of the patient toward those around her.* It is only through sharing and evaluating the positive and negative aspects of the new life that one can come to a realistic appraisal of what lies ahead.

FIND OTHERS WHO UNDERSTAND

Thousands of new mastectomy cases are added to the statistics each year, and most of those patients have valuable advice to offer. Get in touch with former-patient organizations. Ask advice, be open for counsel, share the pent-up emotions. If there are informal group-therapy sessions available, make use of them. Ask for help—but also be willing to share your victories! Thousands of individuals who have experienced similar surgery are ready to assist new patients on a one-to-one basis. The Reach to Recovery Program in the United States and the Mastectomy Association in England are specifically organized to aid mastectomy patients in their psychological and physiological rehabilitation, to make life easier for those in need of help.

Fortunately, not everyone has to go this route. The idea that all those in emotional stress should have the guidance of professional help is wrong. Our own power of choice and our ability to compare our emotional lows to the warning signals as expressed in the phases and components of grief will enable most of us to avoid the severe stress of an unresolved bereavement.

Try, by all means possible, to deal with your bereavement in your own way and in your own time.

Professional therapy should only be considered if all else fails.

CHAPTER EIGHT

Life Is a Chain of New Beginnings

THERE IS HOPE BEYOND GRIEF. Yet this is often forgotten by those in mourning.

"Can you help me bury my husband?" "Can you help me rebuild my life?" and "Is there really a life left without her?" are questions repeatedly asked. But these could have remained unasked if the survivors had been adequately prepared for the psychological repercussions that accompany bereavement.

Experiencing loss is a painful process. Very few can suffer loss and not feel pain. The pain is the reaction to the emotions that accompany a new dimension of life. These emotions should not be hidden behind a façade of indifference. Suppressing the agonies of a loss will postpone their eventual resolution and will prolong the torturous feelings.

So vent your feelings! Let yourself go!

"Oh yes, but that's easy for you to say," you may say. "My grief is different." And it may well be, but that is no reason to accept it without a struggle. When you say your grief is "different," you mean to say your grief is "worse" because it affects you more than it does anyone else, and this makes it even more important for you to have it resolved. Hiding your true inner feelings from those around you and ignoring signals of emotional distress may hurt you. The secret of avoiding a pathological grief reaction is found in confronting the emerging bereavement process in a well-organized fashion, and the starting place for that is at or before the moment of the loss—the instant the pain of separation begins.

No matter how often you may have faced death within the circle of your own family, every time death enters, it hits hard, and there is often that choking sensation in your throat, that empty feeling deep down inside when you begin to realize that you are suddenly a little more alone than you were a few minutes ago.

If the pain is being evoked through the loss of a parent, then it may be complicated by the realization that now *you* are the older generation. But if the loss is that of a spouse or a child, it may appear that the whole world is beginning to cave in, and there is no one to save you.

Sadness and you have suddenly become *one*, and only a few feet away from you there's that great big world filled with nothing but emptiness, and you're feeling alone—so all alone.

You have entered a new world called "sorrow," and the pain that meets you as you reluctantly step across the threshold is overwhelming.

The emotional upheaval that has engulfed you is very real, and no one can understand it but you, and because of that, no one can really empathize with you. There are no degrees of sadness, and everyone experiences his own loss in his own way, and the emptiness you feel is yours and yours alone.

Though others may cry with you, no one can taste your tears.

You have entered what psychologists call the phases of shock and disorganization. Every human being reacts differently to these basic components of the bereavement process, and it is precisely at this point where life and death meet that the first step is being taken on the path to eventual reintegration, even though that step seems to be a long way off.

What should you do when this happens?

The very first thing you must do is share your sorrow. Call someone and explain what happened. Ring a neighbor's doorbell or pick up the phone and call a close friend. You may not fully realize it, but you need both help and support. This is the time when true friendship counts. Ask someone to come to take over. Delegate authority. If there are relatives around you when the death occurs, the shock may be easier to bear, and others can share the responsibility of helping you move through the first difficult days, but if you are alone, just *ask!*

Grievers usually describe the first few hours after the entry of death in many different ways, but the outward reactions are often identical.

The almost uncontrollable crying at various times of the day or night is not only a normal occurrence, but is also to be expected. If the sadness is the result of a major loss, *then you are going to have to cry!* Suppressing it may become a necessity when in the presence of others, but vent it, give in to it when you are alone. Don't break it off halfway, but cry it out—all the way—until your eyes are dry and your cheeks are tear-stained. Women usually find it easier to cry than men, but crying is a release of tension that must be experienced by both sexes. Remember: Crying is not a luxury. It is a necessity! Don't ever put the impulse of giving in to your sadness aside. You may have to postpone it until you are alone, but once it starts, don't hinder it. Keep it going until it finishes of itself. It will fade in and out, start and stop. *It is the beginning of your bereavement process and you will have to work it through.* Stifling it or cutting it off halfway will only cause problems at a later stage. There are no hard dividing lines between the conflicting emotions that you feel. You will recognize anger and aggression, and even though you know intuitively that they are inappropriate to the occasion, they are nevertheless there and you will have to deal with them.

The question as to "how" to deal with all these things does not have a simple answer.

Avoid the idea of rushing into something else to keep your mind off the problem. The stories of the businessman who fights off his sadness by throwing himself totally into his work, or the woman who takes a long vacation just to be in different surroundings, away from everything that keeps the memory of the loss alive, are all too familiar.

Running away has never solved a bereavement problem.

Instead of shielding yourself from the overwhelming emo-

tions, *share them! Recognize them!* If possible, share your grief
with other members of the family. They have also suffered a
loss, and shared grief is easier to deal with than if you are trying
to work through the loss on your own. If the loss occurs in a
family where there is more than one survivor, the grief will have
to be shared with the others, for there is no such thing as shielding each other from the pain caused by an obvious loss. It will
only create separate bastions of sorrow, where each individual
begins to create his own private bereavement problem. Share
your grief, your pain, and above all, your memories! Sharing
your feelings may be one of the most painful experiences of all,
but you will have to do it. In certain cultures the survivor is expected to talk about the deceased. If friends come by and carefully avoid mentioning the loss but instead tell you, "It's the will
of God" or, "It's all for the best," cut them short! Tell them that
you want to talk about the loss; the person who has left you.
Don't focus on the expected platitudes that are usually offered
by those who mean well but don't know how to react. We have
all been in situations where the severity of the loss cannot be
expressed in words. If this is the case, then don't attempt it. Your
bereavement demands that you recognize the loss to the fullest.
And hiding behind carefully worded explanations for the loss
will only hinder the process.

Tell them, "I want to talk about it. I need to talk about it.
Don't be embarrassed when I begin to cry. I need your help to
get through this. Tell me about him. . . ."

In our hurried society, where death is recognized as one of
the inconvenient necessities of life that has to be dealt with, not
enough time is allotted to recover from a loss due to death. Some
countries—the Netherlands, for example—allow the mourner a
three-day "recovery period" with pay. Jewish customs require
the family of the deceased to remain at home for an entire week
to answer all the questions of visiting friends and relatives, fo-
cusing on the loss and discussing it continuously. This forces
the survivors to dwell on it without ceasing, and the sorrow en-

gulfs them time and time again but with a steadily decreasing intensity until it finally extinguishes.

This, however, does not mean that the griever should not be allowed to mourn in private also. A grieving person sometimes needs to be alone, while at other times he or she needs the company of others. Crawling away into isolation to lick our wounds may have its place, but too much social isolation seems to make it more difficult to work through the bereavement process. The griever needs support, but seclusion and withdrawal do not enhance this process.

One griever expressed his feelings this way:

"If I do break down, don't worry. It's part of the process. Sometimes I like to have another person around when I break down, other times I don't. If I should ask you to go away then don't take it personally. Just accept it. It is part of the process. Above all, don't avoid talking to me about 'him.' Don't be afraid to bring up the subject. Don't be afraid that I will break down when you talk about it. I need to break down. I need to talk about it. It's occupying my mind twenty-five hours a day. Don't try to protect me either. You can't protect me. I have to go through this thing whether I like it or not. It's my sorrow, it's my grief and my bereavement. And don't give me clichés. They don't help. Don't tell me, 'It's all for the best.' It's *not* all for the best. Don't give me advice but please be sympathetic. I am an emotional mess right now. . . . Give me understanding . . . that's all I really need."

While going through the bereavement don't avoid seeing the deceased because of the mistaken idea that after seeing him dead, he will only be remembered as he lay in his coffin. If this is among your fears then you have nothing to worry about. A successful bereavement process will erase the painful memories and will allow the happy memories to take on new luster. Don't pay your "last respects" as something that "has to be done."

There is a purpose to it. Viewing the object of your grief in the coffin is a way of breaking through your denial and disbelief that the catastrophe has actually occurred, and a successful bereavement process demands this recognition.

If there are things that should have been said before death, say them NOW! Have an imaginary conversation and set things straight. Tell him how much you love him. Tell him you didn't mean all those things you said before. Tell him good-bye. If he was your husband, spend some time alone with him in the quiet of the funeral parlor and say a last farewell. If she was your child, tell her once more how much you love her, *but say good-bye!*

Often problems arise later on in life because this final leave-taking never took place. The sooner it does, the more successful and speedier the recovery process will be.

Yet viewing of the body is merely the beginning.

After the funeral there will be many situations that will bring you close to the point of breakdown, and you have to force yourself not to avoid them. Force yourself to walk down the streets where you went together; visit the parks where you took your walks; play the music that meant so much to both of you . . . and let the pain come. It will come and fade away, until it finally disappears, never to return. Whatever situation creates painful memories for you, that emotional component will have to be extinguished.

It will never be easy, but it will have to be done.

The most difficult part of all, however, is to erase the memory of the deceased from the home. If you have lived together there will be objects treasured by both, such as mementoes brought home from vacations, a chair, a favorite pipe, his slippers, and above all, photographs. If you have lost a child, her bedroom door may be locked and the room kept exactly as it was when she was still alive. Her clothes are left thrown across the floor, her nightgown still lies in a crumpled fashion at the foot of the bed, and even the bobbypins she stole from your room are kept on the dresser. Despite anyone's advice to the contrary, you keep returning to that room for a moment of repose, for it's there that your memory of her is the strongest.

If you keep that shrine you will never be able to complete your bereavement, for it will only prolong your agony and will prevent you from working through your grief. Your life and the lives of those around you demand that you adjust to the new situation, painful as it may be, You must clean up that room, get rid of the clothes, change the furniture around, turn off that melancholy music, look at the photograph, handle the slippers, sit in that chair. All the objects that will bring you to the point of an emotional breakdown will have to be handled, faced and examined. Every object may bring on a negative reaction, but the same object will become a source of strength once the elicited emotion has been extinguished. At that point understanding will take the place of agony, and the memory will change from bitterness and grief to one that is filled with love and acceptance.

Managing your grief, however, does not always mean that you have been able to turn your life around and have become totally adjusted to the loss. The working through of a bereavement does not leave the survivor unscarred. You have been hurt deeply and only time will be able to smooth the ragged edges of despair. You will still wonder where to go from here.

It is at this point that a sympathetic understanding from close friends and relatives may provide the answer to some, while still others will find consolation in religion, faith in a reunion in the hereafter and supernatural guidance for the difficult days to come. In cases like these, religion can be much more than just a crutch, for a deep faith in a Superior Being who controls all can be a positive factor in the ultimate solution of the grief. But religion provides only one additional source of help, for after every bereavement there are wants and needs, and many of them can be filled only by people, but no one will know of these needs unless you ask for help. Many people have commented that after the attention of the first two weeks following the funeral, "Everything seems just to dry up. Suddenly everyone just stays away . . . and again I am totally alone."

Usually this happens because the griever has not been completely receptive to the many offers of help that were extended during the difficult weeks, and neighbors and friends simply do not know what else to do.

They are not aware of the griever's needs.

Can this be avoided?

It most certainly can. Tell them that you're lonely. Tell them that your courage has faded with the flowers and that your isolation has become unbearable. Don't be ashamed to admit that you need someone to talk to and that your isolation as a barrier of protection is wearing thin. *Remember: The longer you remain alone, the more your friends will drift away until eventually you will be no more to them than another memory from another time.*

Grief is an integral part of life, and we cannot totally separate ourselves from it, but we can prepare for its eventual onslaught by knowing what to avoid.

Remember these guidelines when death grief closes in on you:

- *With the death of a loved one, do not hide your emotions.* Let go. Share your sadness with those around you. Call, phone, cry. Don't deny yourself your moments of intense grief. You need the recognition of the loss. It signals the beginning of your bereavement process.

- *Don't be ashamed of breaking down in front of people you know or when you are alone.* Cry when you feel the need to cry. It is a normal reaction to loss.

  Don't go into isolation or try to lose yourself in your job. Take adequate time to reflect on your sorrow and confront the resulting problems head on. There is no room for denial of reality in your bereavement process.

You have to recognize the severity of the loss and re-shape your life accordingly.

- *Encourage your friends and relatives to talk to you about the deceased.* If they don't do it, keep pressing them. You *need* to talk about him as part of your grieving process in order to come to an eventual extinction of your grief. Hiding from reality will only prolong the process.

- *Don't avoid talking to other members of the immediate family about the loss.* They too need to converse about it in order to start their bereavement extinction process. Share your grief with them so you can mourn and grieve together.

- *Try to see the deceased before the funeral.* If there are things that have remained unsaid, say them now! Spend some time with him to say a last good-bye. Look at him and realize that the end has come and that this is the final separation.

- *Attend the funeral.* The finality of the loss may not sink in until you do.

- *Don't build a shrine!* Building a shrine, a sanctuary for your sorrow, will only prolong the bereavement process and intensify your grief as time goes on. Rearrange the furniture! Play his favorite music! Touch the objects that will cause an emotional breakdown and continue doing so until the elicited emotion finally fades away.

- *Rebuild your life.* Find new friends, new acquaintances and get involved in new activities. Don't rebuild your life on the memory of something that once was, but on the courage and strength you have gained through your bereavement process.

As is the case in bereavement due to death, in divorce

therapy we also must confront difficult situations that have been avoided in the past. The aim is to force a realization that the divorce has actually taken place, eliciting the negative emotions that still bind the partners together, and try to arrive at an extinction process that will eventually fade out these disturbing emotional ties.

In the case of a bereavement due to death, it is well within the scope of the therapy to have the griever say, "I know you're dead. I have to burn you out of my soul and out of my heart. I have to let you go because I cannot go on clinging to you. You have to go. . . . I have to send you away—forever!" It is an essential part of the therapy and a most difficult part of the therapy, *but it has to be done,* and it is being done by everyone who has ever gone through grief therapy. A certain degree of exaggeration is in order so as to eradicate all links with the lost one—and this is true with loss grief caused by divorce as well.

Not every divorcee, however, feels that way. To many it seems totally out of place to create hate feelings when they're really not there, or to stay completely out of touch with each other although they really want to date from time to time. Such attitudes make any attempt at overcoming the loss bereavement ineffectual. The urge to remain together and the desire to be free are contradictory in nature and greatly impede the progress of an eradication of your grief. Many people who find themselves caught in this type of situation tell themselves—and others—that they are being very mature about their divorce and very rational and progressive when they agree to see their ex-partner regularly for casual and sometimes more-than-casual encounters. *What they don't realize is that one of the two will suffer under this sort of arrangement.* Remember: No two partners feel exactly the same way about their divorce, and invariably one of them has a deep hurt that is being aggravated by this "liberated" behavior.

If you want to free yourself from your ex-partner *after* the divorce, then by all means end the casual friendship with him before it can be firmly established. Don't forget that a divorce is the painful ending of a very intimate relationship, and every little hurt is intensified through a maintaining of even the most casual of ties.

Yet, this isn't all. There is much more to ending the marriage ties than that.

Going through the divorce procedure may have been the first big step both of you have taken, but cutting the emotional bond is much more complex.

"Exactly how do I change from a divorcee into being just a 'single girl' again? How can I get rid of the lingering heartache and the smoldering anger that won't go away?"

The lady who asked these questions appeared quite composed, but deep underneath her controlled façade she was an emotional wreck.

Let's be honest. There is no simple remedy for overcoming the heartaches of a traumatic loss, and where two hearts have beaten in unison for many years, the sudden disruptive influence of a divorce can disturb the harmonious cadence of life for many years to come.

But all is not lost! Not by any means! Life isn't over yet!

We are creatures of habit. Our emotional patterns run very much the same way, and we can all learn from each other.

In the chapter on divorce we touched on the close similarity between death grief and divorce grief (also see "Divorce Grief" in the Appendix), and the basic group of components that is common to both can help us avoid the pitfall of a long divorce trauma, provided we're willing to give it a try.

There is no reason in the world why anyone should desire to get stuck in a grieving process, so let's look for the warning spots of trouble.

First of all, there's *anger*. Don't avoid it, but use it as part of the healing process. It's a typical reaction to sorrow and disappointment. Look at anger objectively and examine your motives to see whether it is destructive or constructive. Don't let it devour you from within and control all your actions.

The next point to consider seriously is *jealousy. You have to bring this under total control if your new life is to succeed.* It will be hard to imagine the ex-partner in bed with someone else, *but do it*—until you can live with it! He has a right to it and you have to become so totally free of him that you will be able to accept this. You have to bring all possible fantasies out into the open, exploring them to the fullest, imagining them to the fullest until the elicited emotions tear you apart—until they finally extinguish and you can feel at ease.

The feeling of *shame or embarrassment* is also one that can act as hindrance to the re-establishment of a normal life. When this feeling exists it must be explored carefully and the feelings of shame must be treated the way jealousy is handled until it is extinguished. But surprisingly enough, *throughout the burning-out process flashes of protest and aggression flare up time and time again.* It may come while you are in a period of sinking despair, despondent over what has happened and ashamed of the impression you may be making on your friends and your neighbors.

It may burst forth in desperate cries for understanding, followed by guilt reactions, jealousy and shame. Expressions such as "Why did this happen to me?" and "It was all my fault!" may follow one another in quick succession, and this may only be the beginning of a number of heart-rending emotions.

Reality, however, dictates that there is no shame attached to being divorced. Even though sociologists still report it among symptoms of social disorder, with more than half the population in some areas accepting divorce as an accepted risk of life, it has become the norm. Whether we approve or whether *you* approve is no longer the issue. Shame as an issue in divorce is totally outdated in our society. It is no longer considered shameful to split up a marriage. Hold your head up high! You are not to be despised, nor are you despised! Times have changed!

The phases of *resolution, acceptance* (of the reality) and *reorientation* are not all that separate that they should be regarded totally as free-standing elements of the recovery process. It will take a long time to extinguish all the traces of the parting. Many of them never truly disappear at all. Total recovery may take several years. R. S. Weiss, in *Marital Separation,*[1] divides the entire process of eventual recovery into two distinct phases.

The first one he lists is the *transition phase,* which starts at the moment of separation, lasts eight to ten months and has the characteristic features of disorganization and depression.

Then the *recovery phase* begins, and this may last two to four years. It is during this period that the new identity develops and life begins to take on a new meaning and regularity.

If you are going through a divorce or have gone through one, then you will know that it is a slow process indeed and that Weiss' observation that a minor setback or a stressful situation can seriously affect the recovery is true. It is this second phase, however, that holds the promise for the future, for it is during this time that the former griever opens herself up to the world around her and casts a curious glance at the opportunities awaiting her— wondering *how* to cope, and eventually, with *whom.*

When this happens, life opens its arms anew and stands ready to welcome her all over again.

While these warning signs spell out some of the trouble spots, they are not the only ones to watch out for. The list of grief components includes others equally as im-

portant. Check the list; be on the alert for them, and if
one or more are part of your behavior pattern, elicit them
until they are finally extinguished. Remember: In Guided
Confrontation Therapy the basic process of extinction—
flooding with prolonged exposure—is applicable to all forms
of grief, no matter its cause.

Can we learn anything at all from a grief experience?
We most certainly can.
Only those who can love deeply can grieve deeply. Usually
people do not make great emotional investments easily, but
when they do, they end up giving part of themselves.
To feel, to be committed and to react to the loss of a fellow
human being, someone we love dearly—whether it is through
death or separation—virtually tears us apart.
But be glad of it.
It means that we still have not lost our capacity to love and
to care. It is not their devotion to us but our love for them that
has made us so very vulnerable—and when they die, we die a
little with them because grief cannot exist without love.
But ultimately, whether grief destroys you or strengthens
you is something only you can decide.

Notes

CHAPTER ONE

1. George Engel, "Emotional Stress and Sudden Death," *Psychology Today* (Nov. 1977), p. 118.
2. Doris Kearns, *Lyndon Johnson and the American Dream* (New York: Harper & Row, 1976).
3. Acts 5:5–10.
4. Lionel Tiger, *Optimism: The Biology of Hope* (New York: Simon & Schuster, 1979).
5. I. C. Kaufman and L. A. Rosenblum, "The Reaction of Separation in Infant Monkeys: Anaclitic Depression and Conservation Withdrawal," *Psychosomatic Medicine* (1967), vol. 29, pp. 648–76.
   ———, "Effects of Separation from Mother on the Emotional Behavior of Infant Monkeys," *Annals of the New York Academy of Sciences* (1969), vol. 159, pp. 681–95.
6. C. R. Carpenter, "Societies of Monkeys and Apes," *Biological Symposia* (1942), vol. 8, pp. 177–204.
   G. B. Schaller, "The Behavior of the Mountain Gorilla," in I. De Vore (ed.), *Primate Behavior* (New York: Holt, Rinehart & Winston, 1965).
7. Hans Selye, in personal interview with author Rene Noorbergen (Montreal, Canada, Dec. 23, 1978).
8. Laurence Cherry, "On the Real Benefits of Eustress," *Psychology Today* (Mar. 1978), p. 63.
9. J. Robertson, "A Guide to the Film, 'A Two-year Old Goes to Hospital,'" 3d ed. (London: Tavistock Child Development Research Unit, 1965).

10. T. H. Holmes and R. H. Rahe, "The Social Readjustment Rating Scale," *Journal of Psychosomatic Research* (1967), vol. 11, pp. 213–18.
11. C. C. Madison and A. Viola, "The Health of Widows in the Year Following Bereavement," *Journal of Psychosomatic Research* (1968), vol. 12, pp. 297–306.
12. Beverley Raphael, "Bereavement and Stress: Report to the Health Commission of New South Wales" (Sydney, Australia, 1979).
13. J. Bowlby, *Attachment and Loss, Vol. III, Loss: Sadness and Depression* (London: The Hogarth Press and the Institute of Psycho-analysis, 1980).
14. Sigmund Freud, letter 239 (1929).
15. Depressie, "De Andere Kant," *Nederlands Tijdschrift voor de Psychology en Haar Grensgebieden* (June 1978), vol. 33, no. 4, p. 282.
16. Lorraine D. Siggins, "Mourning: A Critical Survey of the Literature," *International Journal of Psychological Analysis* (1966), vol. 47, p. 14.
17. P. Clayton, "Mortality and Morbidity in the First Year of Widowhood," *Archives of General Psychiatry* (1974), vol. 125, pp. 747–50.
18. J. R. Hodge, "They That Mourn," *Journal of Religion and Health* (1972), vol. 11, pp. 229–40.
19. Raphael, op. cit.
20. E. Lindeman, "Psychiatric Factors in the Treatment of Ulcerative Colitis," *Archives of Neurological Psychiatry* (1945), vol. 53, p. 322.
21. W. D. Rees and S. G. Lutkin, "Mortality of Bereavement," *British Medical Journal* (1967), vol. 4, pp. 13–16.

CHAPTER TWO

1. Anonymous. Copied from a sixteenth-century tombstone.
2. Selby Jacobs and Adrian Ostfelt, "An Epidemiological Review of the Mortality of Bereavement," *Psychosomatic Medicine*

(Sept.–Oct. 1977), vol. 39, no. 5, p. 344.

3. C. M. Parkes, "The Psychosomatic Effects of Bereavement," in O. Hill (ed.), *Modern Trends in Psychosomatic Medicine* (London: Butterworth, 1970).

4. A. Schmale, "Relationship of Separation and Depression in Disease: A Report on a Hospitalized Medical Population," *Psychosomatic Medicine* (1958), vol. 20, pp. 259–77.

5. A. S. Kraus and A. M. Lilienfeld, "Some Epidemiological Aspects of the High Mortality Rate in the Young Widowed Group," *Journal of Chronic Diseases* (1959), vol. 10, pp. 207–17.

6. Ibid.

7. C. M. Parkes, B. Benjamin and R. G. Fitzgerald, "Broken Hearts: A Statistical Study of Increased Mortality Among Widowers," *British Medical Journal* (1969), vol. i, p. 740.

8. Jacobs and Ostfelt, op. cit.

9. M. Young, B. Bernard and G. Wallis, "The Mortality of Widowers," *Lancet* (1963), vol. ii, pp. 454–56.

10. Leshan, 1965, as quoted in Gerald L. Klerman and Judith E. Izen, "The Effects of Bereavement and Grief on Physical Health and General Well-being," *Advanced Psychosomatic Medicine*, (Basel: Karger, 1977), vol. 9, pp. 63–104.

11. Kraus and Lilienfeld, op. cit.

12. C. L. Bacon, R. Renneker and M. Cutler, "A Psychosomatic Survey of the Breast," *Psychosomatic Medicine* (1952), vol. 14, pp. 453–60.

13. Ibid.

14. Kraus and Lilienfeld, op. cit.

15. Ibid.

16. F. P. Paloucek and J. B. Graham, "The Influence of Psychosocial Factors on the Prognosis on Cancer of the Cervix," *Annals of the New York Academy of Sciences* (1965), vol. 125, pp. 814–19.

17. Ibid.

18. A. Schmale and H. Iker, "The Psychological Setting of Uterine Cervical Cancer," *Annals of the New York Academy of Sciences* (1965), vol. 125, pp. 794–801.

19. Ibid.

20. W. Greene, "Psychological Factors and Reticuloendothelial Disease, Part I, Observations on a Group of Men with Lymphomas

and Leukemias," *Psychosomatic Medicine* (1954), vol. 16, p. 220.

21. J. F. Frederick, "Physiological Reactions Induced by Grief," *Omega* (1971), vol. 2, pp. 71–75.

22. Parkes, Benjamin and Fitzgerald, op. cit.

23. Kraus and Lilienfeld, op. cit.

24. G. Engel, "Sudden and Rapid Death During Psychological Stress," *Annals of Internal Medicine* (1971), vol. 74, pp. 771–82.

25. S. E. Cohen and J. Hajioff, "Life Events and the Onset of Acute Closed-angle Glaucome," *Journal of Psychosomatic Res.* (1972), vol. 16, pp. 335–41.

   S. Gifford and J. G. Gunderson, "Cushing's Disease as a Psychosomatic Disorder: A Review of the Literature," *Perspectives on Biological Medicine* (1970), vol. 13, pp. 169–221.

   A. McClary, E. Meyer and E. Weitzman, "Observations on the Role of the Mechanism of Depression in Some Patients with Disseminated Lupus Erythematosus," *Psychosomatic Medicine* (1955), vol. 17, pp. 310–20.

   M. Heiman, "The Role of Stress Situations and Psychological Factors in Functional Uterine Bleeding," *Journal of Mount Sinai Hospital* (1973), vol. 23, p. 154.

   B. Schoenberg, "Psychogenic Aspects of the Burning Mouth," *New York State Dental Journal* (1967), vol. 33, p. 467.

   K. K. Lewin, "The Role of Depression in the Production of Illness in Pernicious Anemia," *Psychosomatic Medicine* (1959), vol. 21, pp. 23–26.

   Kraus and Lilienfeld, op. cit.

   M. Meyerowitz, R. Jacox and D. W. Hess, "Monozygotic Twins Discordant for Rheumatoid Arthritis: A Genetic, Clinical and Psychological Study of Eight Sets," *Arthritis Theum.* (1968), vol. II, pp. 1–21.

   J. J. Kleinschmidt, S. F. Waxenberg and R. Cukor, "Psychophysiology and Psychiatric Management of Thyrotoxicosis: A Two-year Follow-up Study," *Journal of Mount Sinai Hospital* (1965), vol. 23, p. 131.

   E. Lindeman, "Psychiatric Factors in the Treatment of Ulcerative Colitis," *Archives of Neurological Psychiatry* (1945), vol. 53, p. 322.

26. Personal interview with Rene Noorbergen.

CHAPTER THREE

1. M. Roth, "The Phobic Anxiety-Depersonalization Syndrome," *Proceedings of the Royal Society of Medicine* (1959), vol. 52, pp. 587–95.

2. S. Brandon, "An Epidemiological Study of Maladjustment in Childhood," unpublished M.D. thesis (University of Durham, England, 1960).

3. J. R. Averill, "Grief: Its Nature and Significance," *Psychological Bulletin* (1968), vol. 70, pp. 721–48.

4. ———, "An Analysis of Psychosocial Symbolism and Its Influence on Theories of Emotion," *Journal for the Theory of Social Behavior* (1974), vol. 4, pp. 147–90.

   ———, Emotion and Anxiety: Sociocultural, Biological and Psychological Determinants," in M. Zuckerman and C. D. Spielberger (eds.), *Emotion and Anxiety: New Concepts, Methods and Applications* (New York: LEA-John Wiley & Sons, 1976).

5. P. C. Rosenblatt, R. P. Walsh and D. S. Jackson, *Grief and Mourning in Cross-cultural Perspective* (New Haven: HRAF Press, 1976).

6. G. Gorer, *Death, Grief and Mourning in Contemporary Britain* (London: Tavistock Publications, 1965).

7. Ibid.

8. John Bowlby, *Attachment and Loss*, vol. III, *Loss: Sadness and Depression* (New York: Basic Books, 1980).

9. C. M. Parkes, "Recent Bereavement as a Cause of Mental Illness," *British Journal of Psychiatry* (1964), vol. 110, pp. 198–204.

10. D. W. Kay, M. Roth and B. Hopkins, "Aetiological Factors in the Causation of Affective Disorders in Old Age," *Journal of Mental Sciences* (1955), vol. 101, pp. 302–16.

11. C. M. Parkes, *Bereavement: Studies in Grief in Adult Life* (London: Tavistock Publications; New York: International Universities Press, 1972).

    D. Madison, "The Relevance of Conjugal Bereavement to Preventive Psychiatry," *British Medical Journal of Psychology* (1968), vol. 41, pp. 223–33.

    J. Mattison and I. A. C. Sinclair, *Mate and Stalemate: Working with Marital Problems in a Social Services Department* (Oxford: Blackwell, 1979).

12. D. Becker and F. Marjolin, "How Surviving Parents Handled Their Young Children's Adaption to the Crisis of Loss," *American Journal of Orthopsychiatry* (1967), vol. 37, pp. 753–57.

13. P. Marris, *Widows and Their Families* (London: Routledge & Kegan Paul, 1958).

14. R. Bendicksen and R. Fulton, "Death and the Child: An Anterospective Test of the Childhood Bereavement and Later Behavior Disorder Hypothesis," *Omega* (1975), vol. 6, pp. 49–59.

CHAPTER FOUR

1. Maynard Fredelle, "Must Divorce Be So Painful?," *Woman's Day* (March 1974).

2. Ibid.

3. S. Gettleman and J. Markowitz, *The Courage to Divorce* (New York: Ballantine Books, 1974).

4. S. Kessler, *The American Way of Divorce: Prescription for Change* (Chicago, Ill.: Nelson-Hall, 1975).

5. Marlies Terstegge, "Literatuursrapport Echtscheiding." Nederlands Instituut voor Sociaal Sexuologisch Onderzoek, NISSO Literatuursrapport Nr. 11, Zeist, April, 1978.

6. M. Rood-de Boer, "Huwelijk en Echtscheidingsrecht in Nederland," in M. Nevejan and J. Huijts (eds.), *Echtscheiding* (Bussum: Brand, 1969).

CHAPTER SIX

1. V. D. Volkan, A. F. Cilluffo and T. L. Sarvay, "Re-grief Therapy and the Function of the Linking Object as a Key to Stimulate Emotionality," in P. Olsen (ed.), *Emotional Flooding*, Vol. 1 in *New Directions in Psychotherapy* (New York: Human Sciences Press, 1976).

CHAPTER SEVEN

1. Carol Kleiman, "Stress," Orlando (Fla.) *Sentinel Star* (Aug. 19, 1980).
2. Ibid.
3. Susan Brownmiller, *Against Our Will: Men, Women and Rape* (New York: Simon & Schuster, 1975).
4. S. Sutherland and D. Scherl, "Patterns of Response Among Victims of Rape," *American Journal of Orthopsychiatry* (1970), vol. 3, pp. 503–11.
5. A. W. Burgess and L. L. Holmstrom, "Rape Trauma Syndrome," *American Journal of Psychiatry* (1974), vol. 9, no. 6, pp. 981–86.
6. A. Medea and K. Thompson, *Against Rape* (New York: Farrar, Straus & Giroux, 1974).
7. W. H. Masters and V. E. Johnson, *Human Sexual Inadequacy* (Boston: Little, Brown, 1970).
8. Gallup Poll, "Women's Attitudes Regarding Breast Cancer" (Princeton, N.J.: The Gallup Organization, 1974).
9. M. Bard and A. Sutherland, "Psychological Impact of Cancer and Its Treatment, Part IV, Adaptation to Radical Mastectomy," *Cancer* (1955), vol. 8, pp. 656–73.
10. J. Polivy, "Psychological Effects of Mastectomy on a Woman's Feminine Self-concept," *Journal of Nervous and Mental Diseases* (1977), vol. 104, no. 2, pp. 77–88.
11. R. Renneker and M. Cutler, "Psychological Problems of Adjustment to Cancer of the Breast," *Journal of the American Medical Association* (1952), vol. 148, no. 10, pp. 833–39.
12. W. Heyde and P. Aban, "Eheliche Konflikte bei behandelten gynakologischem und Mamma-karzinom," *Praxis der Psychotherapie* (1973), vol. XVIII, no. 2, pp. 49–55.
13. Renneker and Cutler, op. cit.
14. R. Jamison, D. Wellisch and R. Pasnau, "Psychosocial Aspects of Mastectomy: I, The Woman's Perspective," *American Journal of Psychiatry* (1978), vol. 135, no. 4, pp. 432–37.
15. J. B. Jarvis, "Post-mastectomy Breast Phantoms," *Journal of Nervous and Mental Diseases* (1967), vol. 144, no. 4, pp. 266–73.
16. Heyde and Aban, op. cit.
17. G. F. Robbins, S. Holz and J. Trachtenberg, "The Cancer Patient

after Radical Mastectomy," *Cancer Epidemiology and Prevention: Current Concepts* (Springfield: Schottenfield, 1973).

18. C. van Brederode-Ritter and M. Floor, "Als je een borst wordt afgezet. Ervaringen van vrouwen en hulpverleners." Nisso/van Loghum Slaterus (1977).
G. P. Maguire et al., "Psychiatric Problems in the First Year after Mastectomy," *British Medical Journal* (1978), vol. 1, pp. 963–65.

19. T. Morris, S. Greer and P. White, "Psychological and Social Adjustment to Mastectomy: A Two-year Follow-up Study," *Cancer* (1977), vol. 40, pp. 2381–87.

20. D. Frank et al., "Mastectomy and Sexual Behavior: A Pilot Study," *Sexuality and Disability* (1978), vol. 1, no. 1, pp. 16–27.

CHAPTER EIGHT

1. R. S. Weiss, *Marital Separation* (New York: Basic Books, 1975).

Appendix

GROUND RULES FOR GCT

WHEN WE FIRST BEGAN to work with patients according to the principle of Guided Confrontation Therapy, we used to hold to the notion that daily sessions were the best to bring the patient through the agonies of despair and pain as quickly as possible, but experience has shown that for most people daily sessions do not allow sufficient time between sessions to deal emotionally within a given one. Now three fifty-minute sessions per week are thought to be best, even though these are not always easy to schedule. Also, not every patient can handle three therapy sessions per week, for many of them need more time between sessions. In fact, one patient who went through therapy needed up to three weeks to process the emotional upheaval she experienced in the one session before she was ready for the next one. There has to be a balance between the patient's need for processing time and the therapist's desire to help her through her despair as quickly as possible without exhausting her to the point where she becomes totally unable to do any more grief work.

Some grievers tend to shut themselves off from all contact with others and like stricken animals stay in isolation until their wounds have healed. Others seek constant solace and support from those around them, but again, when grief becomes a *problem* and help is required, careful consideration must be given to the various therapies available. Grief therapy according to the principle of Guided Confrontation Therapy has its own set of ground rules, and if you should decide upon this form of intervention, these rules will become the guidelines along which the therapy will be administered.

With experience as the guiding factor these guidelines have been broken down into the following five points:

1. You, as a patient, will not be allowed to break off the treatment halfway. During certain phases of the therapy there may develop a tendency to stop, but this is exactly when you will have to go on. At the beginning of the therapy a certain number of weeks are set within which the therapy should be completed, but in order to be on the safe side, the therapist will multiply that by two. If the therapy is not finished by that time, the time limit will be reset.

2. You may not commit suicide during the course of the treatment. If you want to try it afterward that's your business, but don't attempt it during the course of the therapy. Many patients laugh at this rule, but there have been occasions when it turned out to be germane. The fact that the rule applies only to the duration of the therapy makes it easy to accept and abide by.

3. If there appears to develop an actual danger of suicide or a breaking off of the treatment, you must be prepared for a short period of hospitalization.

4. If during the course of the treatment you become angry with the therapist, you will have to keep in mind that you are not allowed to hit him or break up the furniture.

5. Finally—and this should be regarded as one of the most important points of the agreement—you will be working with the therapist *as a team* on the resolution of a problem: *your grief.* If you feel that the pace is too fast, say so, and the pressure will be eased. If the probing

becomes too painful, then that too can be adjusted. Remember: You will be part of a team. You and the therapist are equal partners in this process!

The basic point that you should not and cannot break off the therapy holds true for both the therapy supplied to you by a professional therapist and the goals and methods you have selected for your own attempt to work yourself out of your grief-related depression. But no matter which method you select, keep in mind that grief therapy is often slowed down by the tranquilizers and antidepressants supplied to you by your family physician. It is difficult enough in any case to break through the buildup of inhibitions, but if you attempt to reach emotions hidden behind an artificial barrier of tranquilizers, the pace of the therapy is slowed down considerably. Because of this, the intake of tranquilizers, antidepressants, sleeping pills *and* alcohol must be reduced to an absolute minimum for the time of the therapy, with no tranquilizers at all on the day of the therapy session.

After outlining the rules and describing the treatment, we, in our practice, supply the prospective client with some printed material on bereavement and ask her to take it home and read it carefully so that she is fully aware of what this treatment entails. We want to be sure that the method of the therapy and the difficulties that will be encountered are well understood. We encourage her to discuss it with others close to her before making a decision to go ahead. If during the next contact the griever indicates that she does desire this form of treatment, we press for another appointment with the griever *and a significant other person in her life*—usually the partner if it concerns the death of a child, or a close relative if it concerns the death of a spouse. If there is a partner, then we regard this contact as vital. If the contact has to come from various family members or friends, then a contact with them may not be necessary. Meeting with a partner can often be extremely important, for it can help the therapist gain valuable understanding of the patterns of the relationship, which may play an important part within the therapy. If the partner is totally aware of what is happening and how and with whom the therapy is being carried out, he will tend to be much more understanding and will be more likely to do the right thing.

During this meeting with the client and the partner, we also emphasize the rule that suicide will not be allowed and also acquaint the partner with the other ground rules of the agreement. Above all, we emphasize to him that he must be easy on the griever, especially during the time of the therapy, and assume as many of her responsibilities as possible. Not making out-of-the-way vacation plans, taking care of the children, and avoiding a hectic social schedule are all part of this total support. The griever must be totally free to concentrate solely on the working through of her bereavement process, for the manner in which she processes her grief during the time between therapy sessions is as important as, if not more important than, the actual grief therapy.

Another issue that should not be overlooked is that the partner should be made aware that there will be definite changes in the relationship following the therapy, especially if the patient's frustration and depression have been of long standing. It is, of course, impossible to predict the exact nature or extent of the changes that will eventually occur, but when someone has been depressed and discouraged for a number of years, and this mood undergoes a drastic change after a few weeks of therapy, then the partner will have to change with it; his attitude will have to adjust accordingly and the adjustments that he has made to deal with the depression will have to be reversed. In a case where both partners have suffered the same loss—the death of a child, for example—we invite both of them to participate in the therapy sessions, but until now this has been consistently declined. In some therapies known to us it has been possible to include the entire family in the process and have them grieve together and solve their bereavement together, but these are not frequent occurrences.

STAGES CONCEPT

Some have challenged the stages concept of grieving. L. A. Bugin writes: "First, the stages are not separate entities, but subsume one another or blend dynamically. Second, the stages are not successive; any individual may experience anger, for instance, prior to denial, or perhaps disorganization before shock. Third, it is not necessary to experience every stage. Depression, or for that matter any volatile emotion, may never be a recognizable response to loss. Fourth, the intensity and duration of any stage may vary idiosyncratically among those who grieve. For one mourner, sadness may be a short-lived experience, while anger is a more protracted stage; the duration of these two emotional stages might be reversed for someone else. Finally, little empirical evidence is offered by proponents to substantiate the theory of stages." ("Human Grief: A Model for Prediction and Intervention," *American Journal of Orthopsychiatry* [1977], vol. 47, no. 2, pp. 196–206.)

SEARCHING BEHAVIOR

As long as the dead person is located somewhere appropriate—in his favorite lawnchair, smoking his pipe while reading a book or accompanying his wife on a shopping spree—there is not much to worry about. About half of all bereaved people experience this as part of their searching behavior. It is when the dead person is "found" somewhere in a spot where he would normally not be expected to be that there may be ground to examine this behavior more closely, since these inappropriate locations can be regarded as pathological. These mislocations are closely related to incomplete mourning. Sometimes these mislocations of the deceased take the form of the husband having "moved into" the body of a close relative; at other times it may be a physical object or even an animal. Dr. Beverley Raphael of the University of Sydney reported on a thirty-five-year-old widow who mislocated her deceased husband in her newborn baby.

"At the time of her husband's death following an operation, Mrs. M. was seven months pregnant with her first child. Soon afterward the baby, a boy, was born prematurely. After Mrs. M.'s return from the hospital with the baby the interviewer called. Although Mrs. M. cried briefly and sadly at times, all her thoughts were on the baby and it soon became evident that she saw the baby as a "reincarnation" of her husband, a word she herself used. She insisted that the baby had 'long fingers just like his father's and a face just like his father's' and that consequently her husband was still with her. Each time the interviewer sought to encourage her to express grief, Mrs. M. insisted the baby represented a replacement of her husband." ("Preventive Intervention with the Crisis of Conjugal Bereavement," M.D. thesis [University of Sydney, Australia, 1976].)

Since in Britain today a belief in reincarnation, in animal form, is held by one in ten of native-born Britons (G. Gorer, *Death, Grief and Mourning in Contemporary Britain* [London: Tavistock Publications, 1965]), it can be expected that many of the mislocations reported in Britain are of this nature. A patient who had developed a chronic emotional disturbance and who had been admitted to a psychiatric hospital following the death of her mother underwent the following experience:

"When her mother died, Mrs. P. consciously directed her search toward making contact with the departed spirit. In company with her sister she improvised a planchette with which she 'received' messages that she believed came from her mother.

"At a seance she noticed a toby jug (a jug made in the shape of a person wearing a large three-cornered hat) that seemed to resemble her mother. She felt that her mother's spirit had entered this jug and she persuaded her sister to give it to her. For some weeks she kept the jug near at hand and had a strong sense of the presence of her mother. However, the jug proved to be a mixed blessing since she found that she was attracted and frightened by it. Her husband was exasperated by this behavior and eventually, against her will, he smashed the jug. His wife noticed that the pieces, which she buried in the garden, 'felt hot'—presumably a sign of life.

"Mrs. P. did not give up her search. Shortly after the jug was broken she acquired a dog. Her mother had always said that if she was ever reincarnated it would be in the form of a dog. When interviewed, Mrs. P. three years later said of the dog, 'She's not like any other animal. She does anything. She'll only go for walks with me or my husband. She seems to eat all the things that Mother used to eat. She doesn't like men.'"

Other mislocations are supposed to happen within the body of the griever, with one reporting that four days after her husband's death, she suddenly felt "something" moving in on her, almost pushing her out of bed. It was so strong, yet so familiar, that she was convinced it was her husband. The feeling eventually disappeared.

DESOLATE PINING

Dr. John Bowlby, the famed psychiatrist who is a pioneer in the field of separation, writes: "For mourning to have a favorable outcome it appears to be necessary for a bereaved person to endure this buffeting of emotion. Only if he can tolerate the pining, the more or less conscious searching, the seemingly endless examination of how and why the loss occurred, and anger at anyone who might have been responsible, not sparing even the dead person, can he gradually recognize and accept that the loss is in truth permanent and that his life must be shaped anew. In this way only does it seem possible for him fully to register that his old patterns of behavior have become redundant and have therefore to be dismantled." (*Attachment and Loss,* vol. III, *Loss: Sadness and Depression.* New York: Basic Books, 1980.)

How difficult this emotional component can be was described by a widow in London, Mrs. X, who recalled that at the beginning, when told of the death of her husband, she had remained perfectly undisturbed and had felt "nothing at all," and that she had been quite surprised to find herself crying later on. Examining her feelings, she admitted that she had consciously avoided giving in to her bereavement because she thought she might not be able to control it once she gave in to it, and that it might even drive her totally insane. She remained perfectly controlled and outwardly composed for three long weeks, after which she suddenly broke down and cried openly in the street. When she was asked to describe her real feelings during those weeks, she said they had been like "walking on the edge of a black pit." (C. M. Parkes, "The First Year of Bereavement," *Psychiatry* [1970], vol. 33, pp. 444–67.)

Ironically, however, in our society mourners are often praised and admired by their family and friends for keeping their composure. This attitude has become known as the "Jackie Kennedy Syndrome." With an iron control over herself, apparently convinced that she was to set an example for the rest of the nation, she went through her period of public mourning without any open or outward sign or display of grief—but it must have been there nevertheless. Her grief must have been overwhelming, yet she did not reveal it to the outside world. Her reaction was undoubtedly misjudged by millions of viewers to be the correct attitude in the case of sudden death, and it may well have created havoc in the lives of thousands of grievers

DESPAIR

The symptoms of this emotional component of grief are not so easily explained. During this period in the mourning process the individual is in the throes of intense mental anguish, and the ability of the body to withstand stress and fight disease is greatly reduced. Also, the general apathy and the desire to withdraw from all social interaction block all possible efforts to break with the past or create new contacts. The symptoms associated with this component have been thought of as a conservation-withdrawal technique of the body and may be the result of the experience of helplessness and hopelessness. It is part of the defense mechanism of the human organism which, when carried to the extreme, can result in depressive character disorders.

GUILT

In the area of pathological grief, intense and complete preoccupation with guilt is the overwhelming response to loss. Here no true sadness is experienced or expressed, yet there usually is an intense search for meaning or understanding of death. Major guilt is often connected with extreme ambivalence in the preexisting relationship, where the verbalized death wishes appear to have had the desired result.

The following case is a typical example.

Mrs. T.'s relationship with Mr. T. was intensely ambivalent from the outset. He was sadomasochistic in his torturing behavior and abuse of her. She, on the other hand, was rigidly bound by her attachment to sexual cathexis in him.

Three weeks before his death, Mrs. T. finally left him, determined to get a divorce, and told him in their final argument to "kill yourself with your car."

When Mrs. T. resisted all attempts at reconciliation, her husband decided to grant her wish and actually committed suicide by gassing himself in the family car. Her feeling of guilt was severe, and it took several counseling sessions before she was even able to admit that she had really made that wish and that she indeed bore a share of the guilt. Her dislike of him had been so strong that following the therapy she was able to admit that she knew that she "would only ever be really free if he died."

DENIAL PHASE

The denial phase, or the "phase of disbelief," as it is also known, contains several elements that add to the complexity of this phase. The "denial" or the "disbelief" is naturally first directed toward the loss itself. Statements such as, "I can't believe it's happened!" and "God wouldn't let that sort of thing happen to us!" are among the first reactions. None of us is anxiously looking forward to the moment when we will be involved in a tragedy, and if and when it happens, disbelief and denial are very natural human reactions. But useful as they may be, they delay the healing process and have the tendency to lengthen the duration of the pain. If the loss comes at the end of a long illness of someone who was still in the prime of life, then the accuracy of the medical diagnosis may also become the target of the denial, as well as the competency of the medical staff. Combine these elements with the denial of the emotions connected with the loss, and the denial phase can mean much more than a mere reluctance to accept the death of a loved one. In this phase, many people suppress their feelings or cannot feel the anger, grief or guilt. Psychological counseling will often be needed to stimulate the griever into feeling once again.

PHOBIAS

A buildup of dog phobia can just as well develop into agoraphobia, the fear of being in open places—that is, away from the safety of home. Going out increases tension because there are more demands made on you; there are more stimuli to take into account; there is more traffic outside; there are lots of irritating noises; people bump into you on the bus or in the stores; you feel crowded, uncomfortable, start feeling faint, can't get enough air and you desperately want to get back home where you are in full control.

As a result you begin to avoid situations that make those demands on you. Within the protection of your own four walls you meet only those people with whom you feel comfortable, and consequently there is less information for you to process. Home is safer—at least that's the way it appears to you!

Outcome? Agoraphobia as the result of an unresolved bereavement process.

RAPE TRAUMA

For a number of years now, psychologists have attempted to group the various emotional reactions of this typical psychological trauma syndrome into a number of clearly identifiable phases and have finally been able to assemble them into four distinct units known as *acute reactions, outward adjustment, integration and resolution.*

While on the surface they do not appear to be totally identifiable with our phases and components of the bereavement process, there is nevertheless a remarkable degree of resemblance.

A closer look will confirm this.

ACUTE REACTIONS

Under *acute reactions* are usually listed the reactions that are experienced during the hours or days immediately following the rape. These reactions include such emotional components as shock, disbelief and dismay. When a victim is in this stage, she is usually highly agitated, incoherent and unable to give a reasonable account of what has happened to her. She will almost invariably break down whenever the incident is mentioned. The duration of this phase is variable but lasts normally no longer than a few days to a week. In this period victims often wonder who to tell and what to tell, and are certain that no one will really understand what they are going through.

OUTWARD ADJUSTMENT

The phase of *outward adjustment* is just that: outward adjustment. It does not imply that anything has changed. This phase contains a heavy measure of denial and suppression, ignoring what has happened, as if that will erase it completely from the victim's history. It does not indicate a final solution of the traumatic event. While passing through this stage the victim begins to examine her own feelings toward the assailant, wondering why it all happened and attempting to subdue the growing feelings of anger and resentment that keep coming to the surface. It is also during this time that she will attempt to shrug aside her feelings of doubt as to her own role in the assault.

INTEGRATION

The third phase, *integration*, begins when the victim develops an inner sense of depression and expresses an urgent need to communicate with those around her. She will make a serious attempt to resolve the feelings that have been aroused by the rape, and will begin to scrutinize the related issues that she has tried to suppress up to this point.

RESOLUTION

It is during the *resolution* phase that the victim will have to take a good, hard look at herself and realize that she must begin to accept the event as an undeniable part of her life, and furthermore that she will have to come to a realistic appraisal of her own degree of complicity in the act. Statements such as, "I shouldn't have gone out alone; they told me something like this might happen but I knew better," and "It was stupid of me to walk through that dark street. I really asked for it this time" are commonly heard during this phase and must be resolved if full reintegration is to occur. Also, her attitude toward the assailant and her relationship to him, as well as the degree of enjoyment she experienced during the rape no matter how limited, must be re-examined. She must realize that if she ever tried to "understand" the actions of the rapist, this must end

NOW. There is place for anger toward him for having committed the act, and anger toward herself for having permitted it, and these feelings must be vented before they can be resolved.

In schematic form the comparison between the phases and components of death grief and those of rape trauma are extremely similar, and look like this:

Phases and Components of Death Grief	*Phases and Components of Rape Trauma*
Shock	Shock
Disorganization	Disbelief
Searching behavior	Dismay, despair
Emotional components	Suppression
Desolate pining	Anger
Despair	Resentment
Guilt	Guilt
Anxiety	Anxiety
Jealousy	Depression
Shame	Resolution
Aggression	Acceptance
Protest	Reintegration
Letting go	
Resolution and acceptance	
Reintegration	

(Death Grief: Denial brackets Searching behavior through Protest; Rape Trauma: Denial brackets Disbelief through Depression)

Only if all the emotional components that are part of the rape trauma have been worked through successfully to the point of extinction can total reintegration finally take place.

MASTECTOMY GRIEF

In drawing a straight comparison between the various causes of grief, we find a remarkable degree of similarity, but while the underlying principles are the same, mastectomy trauma presents us with a decided shift in emotional reactions. Also,

the frequency and intensity as well as the duration of the
phases of various grief components can vary greatly.

Shock

The moment a woman discovers the first signs of cancer
and has been informed by her physician that she must be admitted to a hospital for an exploratory operation, she is benumbed, worried, tense and anxious. (G. F. Robbins, S. Holz
and J. Trachtenberg, "The Cancer Patient After Radical Mastectomy," *Cancer Epidemiology and Prevention: Current Concepts* [Springfield: Schottenfeld, 1973].) The very thought of
losing a breast is something that seems almost akin to death.
This feeling of shock remains with the woman until after the
operation when she realizes that it was indeed cancer, and one
or both of her breasts have actually been removed. At this stage
sorrow, fear of further cancer complications, pain, uncertainty
and many other emotions vie for attention, and even thoughts
of suicide are often reported during this time. (R. E. Renneker
et al., "Psychoanalytical Explorations of Emotional Correlates
of Cancer of the Breast," *Psychosomatic Medicine* [1963], vol.
XXV, no. 2, pp. 106, 124.)

Disorganization

It may take a few days, but once the shock has worn off,
the patient enters a phase of disorganization and becomes caught
in an avalanche of conflicting and confusing emotions. Every
woman reacts in her own way during this period, ranging from
lethargic indifference to hyperactivity (M. Bard and A. Sutherland, "Psychological Impact of Cancer and Its Treatment," Part
IV, "Adaptation to Radical Mastectomy," *Cancer* [1955], vol.
8, pp. 656–73); her own defensive capabilities and her own
method of coping with unexpected calamities will guide her
through this phase.

Searching Behavior

As is the case with bereavement as a result of death, bereavement due to loss also results in a restlessness that can only be described as "searching behavior." Some women keep wandering away from home, walking, bicycling, driving aimlessly, while others begin to experience the feeling that nothing has changed; that the amputated breast is still there. (S. Weinstein, R. Better and E. Serson, "Phantoms Following Breast Amputation," *Neuropsychologia* [1970], vol. 8, pp. 185–97.) Known as a phantom experience, this feeling is not at all unusual. One researcher reported that phantom experiences were reported by 33.5 percent out of 203 women, while another reported 23 percent out of 104 patients. (J. B. Jarvis, "Post-mastectomy Breast Phantoms," *Journal of Nervous and Mental Diseases* [1967], vol. 144, no. 4, pp. 226–73.) Some patients reported "feeling" the nonexistent breast at least once per day, others once per month. It is interesting that this feeling may persist for years. Interviews that were conducted four years after mastectomies revealed that 70.6 percent of the women questioned were still not totally free from phantom experiences. (Weinstein et al., op. cit.) It is also during this phase of the bereavement process that many women develop the conviction that the body has become extremely sensitive since the operation. Abeel van Voorst Vader holds the opinion that these phantom experiences can be regarded as part of the searching for the lost breast.

Fear

Fear is a component that accompanies breast cancer from the moment of discovery to the final moment of reintegration—fear of everything connected with cancer. The fear that she will be losing her breasts and may die holds her in an iron grip (H. S. Goldsmith and E. S. Alday, "Role of the Surgeon in the Rehabilitation of the Breast Cancer Patient," *Cancer* [Dec. 14–17, 1971]); worry that her husband will no longer regard her as an adequate sex partner (Robbins et al., op. cit.), fear that her own body will frighten her and fear that her children will not appreciate her any longer are all basic to the emotional upheaval that follows the operation. She is all alone in her fear of the future, and no one can take this away from her. The fear of a recurrence of cancer may become so strong that it may form the basis for one or more phobias (Bard and Sutherland, op. cit.), while the fear that others will notice that she has undergone a disfiguring operation may lead to feelings of inferiority.

EMBARRASSMENT OR SHAME

Shame because she has lost a breast is an emotion no woman seems to be able to avoid. The moment she is released from the hospital to rejoin her family at home, the fear that her husband will be repulsed when he sees the scar will be joined by the shame that she is no longer a "complete woman." "Sex has lost its meaning for me; he will never understand how I really feel," and "I am so ashamed of how I look" are typical comments of women after mastectomies. This feeling often results in turning her back toward her husband while changing clothes (A. Torrie, "Like a Bird with Broken Wings," *World Medicine* [1970], vol. 5, pp. 36–48), making love with a blouse on and the lights off, and not looking at herself in the mirror while bathing. There are exceptions, but they are rare. As one woman reported when questioned about her relationship with her husband after her double mastectomy, "We've been married twenty years. He knows I am a woman; I know he is a man. The removal of my breasts has not changed this at all. We're still the same to one another."

Shame or embarrassment, however, is not limited to the immediate surroundings. It is felt when others press for details of the operation. It is also felt when meeting close friends for the first time since the hospitalization.

"Will they notice my disfigurement? Will they know how I look underneath my blouse?" are silent questions that remain unspoken, but they are born out of shame—unfounded as it may be.

Desolate Pining

Some of the most common reactions that appear soon after the mastectomy are crying, a feeling that life has ended, a desperate feeling of "not belonging anymore" and that no one cares (*ibid.*). Deepening feelings of loneliness and sorrow, hopelessness and helplessness as well as an increasing inferiority complex often lead to an increased use of tranquilizers, sleeping pills and alcohol. "I wouldn't be able to live with myself in this new form if I didn't have my tranquilizers," one woman recently commented when asked about her psychological adjustment to her operation. "I am ugly, hideous, monstrous! I hide from my children whenever I want to get undressed, and I'd scream if I didn't have something to make me relax. The thought that I have to live this way until I die is more than I can take." (Rene Noorbergen, personal files.)

Despair

The hopelessness that is part of the emotion of despair has been described as a broken vase that cannot be repaired, or as a bird with broken wings. It is difficult to find a more apt description. The feeling is often so strong that everything is done to hide the source of this despair, and it may be because of this that of the fourteen hundred mastectomized women questioned in one survey, 30 percent admitted to hiding their scars from their husbands (A. Torrie, op. cit.). Feelings that life is now without meaning and that suicide may be the best way to end her prolonged emotional crisis can occur during this stage.

Guilt

Guilt is a component that may occur at various points of the bereavement process and is often based on the feeling that the mastectomy might not have taken place if medical help had been sought at an earlier stage. "If I had only gone to the doctor sooner," and "What have I done to my marriage?" are heard repeatedly before a new adjustment is made.

JEALOUSY

This component is often found in bereavement due to death when the widow is jealous of the women who still have their husbands or their children. It is, however, rarely mentioned as a component in the emotional aftermath of a breast amputation, but it exists nevertheless.

"I won't say that I am exactly worried about my husband," one patient reluctantly admitted, "but I do wonder how he feels when he sees a woman with both her breasts parading around the swimming pool. I often wonder, 'Why me and not her?'" Another one wondered, "When I see one of my colleagues who is well endowed and then think of the way I look underneath my prosthesis, then I feel jealous. Sure, why not? After all, I was once that way—but look at me now!"

PROTEST AND AGGRESSION

Protest is a normal reaction. No one wants to become a cancer statistic. The aggressive feelings that accompany this protest are the most difficult to handle, and the patient often turns on the family as if they are partially to blame for what has happened (Bard and Sutherland, op. cit.). The patient may also aggressively react to the limited choice of clothing available to her or when friends suddenly regard her as a permanent patient. The feeling of inability to perform tasks that were routine before also adds to the buildup of aggression.

DENIAL

As is the case with other forms of loss, denial plays an important role throughout the bereavement process. Many women stubbornly refuse to admit to themselves that they have actually undergone a mastectomy. The refusal to look at herself in the mirror, hiding the scar from her husband, the recurring phantom feelings and the undressing in the dark or in a dark closet are all examples of this denial syndrome. Even the rush to the plastic surgeon is a form of denial.

RESOLUTION AND ACCEPTANCE

This can take place only when all the difficult-to-cope-with emotions have been resolved. When the aggression toward the loved ones, the denial of the loss, the inferiority complex and the refusal to look at the inflicted wound, to name but a few, have been resolved and have given way to a total acceptance of the new reality, then life will once again become manageable.

REINTEGRATION

Reintegration of someone who has undergone a mastectomy is not so much an act on her side as a decided act on the side of those who have neglected to give her the full understanding and the emotional support she has needed. Only when both sides work toward breaching the gap that has been created by the surgery can a conscious attempt at total reintegration become a fact.

DIVORCE GRIEF

In divorce grief we deal with very much the same components as the other grief areas: death and "other losses." The *anger* that apparently cannot be separated from divorce grief can be extremely strong, and its vengeful strength makes divorcees often wonder whether they are losing their mind. In reality, however, it is a reaction that is well within reason, and it is quite normal to harbor those feelings whatever the length

of the marriage. It is a typical reaction to sorrow and disappointment, and it definitely has its positive aspects. If you can reach
the point where you are willing to accept these conflicting
emotions and regard them as natural parts of the divorce-
bereavement process, you are well on the way to independence.
As long as you don't recognize the importance of anger as part
of the bereavement, there is every chance that the process will
stagnate. Since too much anger may devour a person from
within, it becomes the primary concern in divorce-associated
grief. Eventually the anger will disappear—and other feelings
will take its place.

Guilt is one that replaces it. It can be caused by a variety
of reasons, not only for the conviction that the marriage could
have succeeded if she had only tried a little harder, but also
guilt for the problems the separation has caused the partner,
and guilt for having agreed to the divorce in the first place.

Thoughts of "If I only had . . ." and "If I had not . . ."
continue to surface with increasing regularity and assume
frightening proportions. In their book *The First Year of Bereavement* (New York: John Wiley & Sons, 1974), I. O. Glick,
R. S. Weiss and C. M. Parkes call this phase "obsessive hind-
sight"—always occupied with the same thought, always attempting to recall certain events from times past, the continuing
search for answers and explanations, and the final question as
to whether it all could have been avoided. Often guilt begins
to make its appearance before the anger has completely dis-
solved, although anger is such an all-consuming emotion that it
nearly overshadows all other components until it is totally and
ultimately extinguished.

Anger and guilt weave in and out during the extinction
process and need to be experienced and worked through in a
bereavement process. The two separate components of anger,
dysfunctional and functional, become almost insurmountable
barriers in therapy, for the dysfunctional aspect of anger manifests itself in a destructive way and is full of vengeance and
hatred, which are shown in the way the battles for child sup-

port, visitation rights, alimony and division of property are fought. The functional aspect of anger is shown in the protective quality of being able to vent the emotions. It is a reaction to the feelings of loss, fear, helplessness or guilt.

Revealing these emotions unreservedly brings the hurt out in the open.

Depression too can be highly complex, and that it is not without cause can readily be seen. Through the divorce process, the parents have deprived their children of a united family. They feel they have disappointed them and in some ways have violated the sacred marriage contract. Although divorce is no longer regarded as a total disgrace, a general prejudice against divorce still exists even in our enlightened Western society. Sociologists routinely include the divorce statistics among those on crime, juvenile delinquency, drug addiction and mental disorder as symptoms of social disorder, and there is no move pending to change this classification process. We have to face the fact that in some ways we still live in a family-oriented culture. The traditional family ties in countries such as the United States and those in Europe are so highly respected that, as far as we have been able to determine, no voices were raised in protest when a publication such as *Psychiatric Care,* Volume XII (1974), suggested: "Society questions the single person's sense of responsibility, his or her desirability as an employee, tenant, neighbor, customer and even as a client. . . . Moreover, the stereotype of the unmarried woman," the article continued, "is either as promiscuous or frigid, and the bachelor as indulging himself with heterosexual or homosexual pleasures."

Whether "society" *really* felt that way, even in 1974, is something that can surely be questioned!

If "society," however, feels that way about those who have not as yet married, how much more judgmental must it be to those who have married and have failed in their quest for happiness. It fans the flames of depression and sears the psyche of the bereaved like a branding iron. There is no doubt that a divorce has a greater detrimental effect on the woman than on the man. Quite often the marriage is *the* thing in the life of a woman, whereas the male partner has his job and his professional connections to occupy most of his time. A divorce does not seem to affect this part of his life at all.

A woman, however, faces an entirely different situation. For her, the first few months of a divorce are often the most difficult to endure because she has lost a major share of her identity and must try to re-establish herself. It is a matter of survival. A woman experiencing the realities of a divorce has justification for being depressed, for financial problems, credit problems, legal problems and social isolation all seem to besiege her at the same time, and lacking money, advice and direction, she may find it difficult to begin to put the pieces of a broken life back into order.

The area of *jealousy* as a component can also cause a great deal of concern, for it invariably centers on the unjustified fears that he might have a relationship with someone else, and this imaginary development intensifies until she reaches the point where she is "seeing" him in bed with his newfound love, and then all the smoldering emotions of hate, jealousy, envy, disgust and vengeance seem to melt into one all-encompassing burst of uncontrolled jealousy.

Index

Physical loss. *See* Loss from surgery or accident; Mastectomy
Physiology, stress and, 28–30
Postmastectomy patient. *See* Mastectomy
Protest, mastectomy grief and, 202
PSE. *See* Dektor-101 Psychological Stress Evaluator
Psychiatric symptoms, of surviving spouse, 35–36. *See also* Pathological grief
Psychoanalysis, compared with Guided Confrontation Therapy, 18
Psychosomatic disease, 61–62; life crises and, *see* "Social Readjustment Rating Scale"; and surviving spouse, 35. *See also* Illness

Quarrel, before fatality, 69

Rahe, Dr. R. H., 32, 36, 87
Ramsay, Dr. Ronald W., 17
Rape: defined, 150; incidence, 151. *See also* Rape trauma
Rape trauma: acute reactions to, 195; compared with death grief, 197; and Guided Confrontation Therapy, 150–153; phases of, 195–197
Raphael, Dr. Beverley, 35, 189–190
Reach to Recovery Program, 162
Recovery process, 40; and divorce, 175
Rees, Dr. W. D., 45–47
Refugees. *See* Loss of country
Reincarnation, 190
Reintegration, 72; and mastectomy grief, 203
Remarriages, 96–97

Renneker, R. E., 198
Reorganization, in children, 77–78
Reorientation, divorce and, 175
Replacements, 190
Resolution, 72; and divorce, 175; and mastectomy grief, 203; and rape trauma, 196–197
Richter, Curt, 24
Robbins, G. F., 198
Robertson, J. A., 31–32
Rood-de Boer, M., 99

Schmale, Dr. A., 50, 56
Searching behavior, 67, 189–191; and mastectomy grief, 199
Second marriages, 96–97
Self-esteem, 147
Selye, Dr. Hans, 26–28, 29–31, 61
Serson, E., 199
Sex differences: and impact of divorce, 205–206; and pathological bereavement, 74
Sexual difficulties, mastectomy and, 158
Sexual freedom, divorce and, 98
Sexual relations: after mastectomy, 161; with divorced partner, 89
Shah of Iran, 59
Shame, 70; and divorce, 95–96, 174–175. *See also* Embarrassment
Shock, 66, 67, 164; and mastectomy grief, 198
Single person, social attitudes toward, 205
"60 Minutes," 17, 101
Smale, Dr. Arthur, 24
Social network, value of, 67. *See also* Family; Friends and relatives